Planning and Selection for Electrical Systems

Malcolm Doughton and John Hooper

CENGAGE
Learning

Australia • Brazil • Japan • Korea • Mexico • Singapore • Spain • United Kingdom • United States

CENGAGE
Learning·

Planning and Selection for Electrical Systems
Malcolm Doughton and John Hooper

Publishing Director: Linden Harris

Commissioning Editor: Lucy Mills

Editorial Assistant: Claire Napoli

Project Editor: Alison Cooke

Production Controller: Eyvett Davis

Marketing Executive: Lauren Mottram

Typesetter: S4Carlisle Publishing Services

Cover design: HCT Creative

Text design: Design Deluxe

For product information and technology assistance,
contact **emea.info@cengage.com.**

For permission to use material from this text or product,
and for permission queries,
email **emea.permissions@cengage.com.**

British Library Cataloguing-in-Publication Data
A catalogue record for this book is available from the British Library.

ISBN: 978-1-4080-3991-5

Cengage Learning EMEA
Cheriton House, North Way, Andover, Hampshire, SP10 5BE
United Kingdom

Cengage Learning products are represented in Canada by Nelson Education Ltd.

For your lifelong learning solutions, visit **www.cengage.co.uk**

Purchase your next print book, e-book or e-chapter at
www.cengagebrain.com

Printed in Malta by Melita Press
1 2 3 4 5 6 7 8 9 10 – 14 13 12

Dedication

This series of study guides is dedicated to the memory of Ted Stocks whose original concept, and his publication of the first open learning material specifically for electrical installation courses, forms the basis for these publications. His contribution to training has been an inspiration and formed a solid base for many electricians practising their craft today.

The Electrical Installation Series

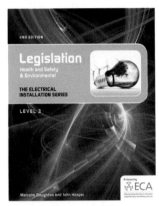

Legislation: Health and Safety & Environmental

Organizing and Managing the Work Environment

Principles of Design Installation and Maintenance

Installing Wiring Systems

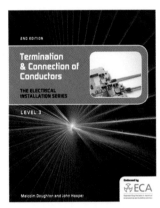

Termination and Connection of Conductors

Inspection Testing and Commissioning

Fault Finding and Diagnosis

Maintaining Electrotechnical Systems

Contents

About the authors

Malcolm Doughton

Malcolm Doughton, I.Eng, MIET, LCG, has experience in all aspects of electrical contracting and has provided training to heavy current electrical engineering to HNC level. He currently provides training on all aspects of electrical installations, inspection, testing, and certification, health and safety, PAT and solar photovoltaic installations. In addition Malcolm provides numerous technical articles and is currently managing director of an electrical consultancy and training company.

John Hooper

John Hooper spent many years teaching a diverse range of electrical and electronic subjects from craft level up to foundation degree level. Subjects taught include: Electrical Technology, Engineering Maths, Instrumentation, P.L.C.s, Digital, Power and Microelectronic Systems. John has also taught various electrical engineering subjects at both Toyota and JCB. Prior to lecturing in further and higher education he had a varied career in both electrical engineering and electrical installations.

Acknowledgements

The authors and publisher would like to thank Chris Cox and Charles Duncan for their considerable contribution in bringing this series of study guides to publication. We extend our grateful thanks for their unstinting patience and support throughout this process.

The authors and publisher would also like to thank the following for providing pictures for the book:

Cooper Bussmann (UK) Ltd
Eaton Electric Limited
Hager Ltd

The IET/BSI (for figure 2.6) Permission to reproduce extracts from BS 7671:2008 is granted by the Institute of Engineering and Technology (IET) and (BSI). No other use of this material is permitted. BS 7671:2008 Incorporating Amendment No 1: 2011 can be purchased in hardcopy format only from the IET website http://electrical.theiet.org/ and the BSI online shop: http://shop.bsigroup.com

MK Electric
TLC Direct

This book is endorsed by:

Representing the best in electrical engineering and building services

Founded in 1901, the Electrical Contractors' Association (ECA) is the UK's leading trade association representing the interests of contractors who design, install, inspect, test and maintain electrical and electronic equipment and services.

www.eca.co.uk

Study guide

This study guide has been written and compiled to help you gain the maximum benefit from the material contained in it. You will find prompts for various activities all the way through the study guide. These are designed to help you ensure you have understood the subject and keep you involved with the material.

Where you see 'Sid' as you work through the study guide, he is there to help you and the activity 'Sid' is undertaking will indicate what it is you are expected to do next.

Task

Before continuing with this chapter go to BS 7671, Appendix 3 and familiarize yourself with the currents required for the various devices to disconnect within the times required.

Task A 'Task' is an activity that may take you away from the book to do further research either from other material or to complete a practical task. For these tasks you are given the opportunity to ask colleagues at work or your tutor at college questions about practical aspects of the subject. There are also tasks where you may be required to use manufacturers' catalogues to look up your answer. These are all important and will help your understanding of the subject.

Try this

Draw a circuit diagram for a:

a normally closed circuit with four call points

_____

b normally open circuit with four call points

_____

Try this A 'Try this' is an opportunity for you to complete an exercise based on what you have just read, or to complete a mathematical problem based on one that has been shown as an example.

Remember

A current flow of 0.05A, that is 50 milliamps, is enough to cause a fatal electric shock. So protection against even very small currents is vital to prevent danger from electric shock.

Remember A 'Remember' box highlights key information or helpful hints.

RECAP & SELF ASSESSMENT

Circle the correct answers.

1 The current drawn by a 9.2kW load with a power factor of 0.8 connected to a 230 volt supply is:

   a. 50 A

   b. 45 A

   c. 40 A

   d. 32 A

2 A correction factor of 0.725 is applied when the overcurrent protection is provided by a:

   a. BS 88 fuse

   b. BS 1361 fuse

   c. BS 3036 fuse

   d. BS EN 60898 m.c.b.

Recap & Self Assessment At the beginning of all the chapters, except the first, you will be asked questions to recap what you learned in the previous chapter. At the end of each chapter you will find multichoice questions to test your knowledge of the chapter you have just completed.

Note

The line to line voltage is equal to the sum of the two line to neutral voltages each multiplied by sine 120° (voltages displaced by 120°). The sine of 120° is 0.866 which is equal to half $\sqrt{3}$. As there are two L-N voltages displaced by 120° we have the line to neutral voltage $\times \sqrt{3}$.

Note 'Notes' provide you with useful information and points of reference for further information and material.

This study guide has been divided into Parts, each of which may be suitable as one lesson in the classroom situation. If you are using the study guide for self tuition then try to limit yourself to between 1 hour and 2 hours before you take a break. Try to end each lesson or self study session on a Task, Try this or the Self Assessment Questions.

When you resume your study go over this same piece of work before you start a new topic.

Where answers have to be calculated you will find the answers to the questions at the back of this book but before you look at them check that you have read and understood the question and written the answer you intended to. All of your working out should be shown.

At the back of the book you will also find a glossary of terms which have been used in the book.

A 'progress check' at the end of Chapter 2, and an 'end test' covering all the material in this book, are included so that you can assess your progress.

There may be occasions where topics are repeated in more than one book. This is required by the scheme as each unit must stand alone and can be undertaken in any order. It can be particularly noticeable in health and safety related topics. Where this occurs read the material through and ensure that you know and understand it and attempt any questions contained in the relevant section.

You may need to have available for reference current copies of legislation and guidance material mentioned in this book. Read the appropriate sections of these documents and remember to be on the look-out for any amendments or updates to them.

Your safety is of paramount importance. You are expected to adhere at all times to current regulations, recommendations and guidelines for health and safety.

Unit five

Planning and selection for electrical systems

Material contained in this unit covers the knowledge requirement for C&G Unit No. 2357-304 (ELTK 04a), and the EAL unit QELTK3/004a.

Planning and selection for electrical systems considers the practices and procedures for the preparation and installation of wiring systems. It considers the types, applications and limitations of wiring systems and associated equipment and the procedures for selecting tools, equipment and fixings. It also covers the regulatory requirements which apply to the installation of wiring systems, associated equipment and enclosures.

You could find it useful to look in a library or online for copies of the legislation and guidance material mentioned in this unit. Read the appropriate sections and remember to be on the lookout for any amendments or updates to them. You will also need to have access to manufacturers' catalogues for wiring systems, tools and fixings.

Before you undertake this unit read through the study guide on page vii. If you follow the guide it will enable you to gain the maximum benefit from the material contained in this unit.

1

Supply systems

LEARNING OBJECTIVES

This chapter considers the characteristics and application of consumer supply systems and the arrangements for isolation, switching and protection. You will need to refer to BS 7671 and IET Guidance Note 1, when you are working through this chapter.

On completion of this chapter you should be able to:

● Explain the characteristics and applications of:

   – earthing arrangements

   – supply systems.

● Explain the arrangements for electrical installations and systems with regard to provision for:

   – isolation and switching

   – overcurrent protection

   – earth fault protection.

Part 1 Earthing arrangements

Before we consider the earthing arrangements we need to understand why and how we earth the electrical supply system.

It is generally accepted that the earth we walk and build on is a conductor of electricity and as we have no choice over this we need to consider it very seriously.

The mass of earth is generally accepted as being at a potential of zero volts, and, as our electrical installations operate at voltages above zero, there is a potential difference between the mass of earth and our electrical system. In order to control any current flow which may occur to the mass of earth, we need to connect it to our system and provide a reference for the earth. To achieve this all electricity substations have the star (neutral) point connected to earth.

It is also a requirement that all electrical installations have a connection to earth. The consumer's earth connection may be provided by the Distribution Network Operator (DNO). This provision may be by connection to the metal sheath of the supply cable or a separate conductor within the supply cable. Systems using this provision are referred to as TN-S systems. Alternatively, the earth provision may be provided by use of the neutral within the supplier's network and these systems are referred to as TN-C-S or PME systems.

Where the consumer's earth connection is not provided by the supplier then a separate installation earth electrode must be installed and the system is referred to as a TT system. In this case it is normal practice to fit a residual current device (RCD) to protect the installation.

We shall be considering these public supply systems in more depth later in this chapter.

Earth faults

Earth faults are generally caused by live parts coming into contact with exposed metalwork which is then made live. In order to prevent this dangerous situation from arising we connect the exposed metalwork to earth. The reason for this is to provide a safe return path for earth fault currents.

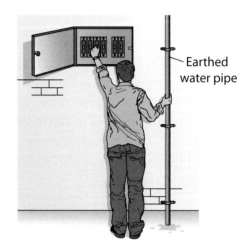

Earthed water pipe

Figure 1.1 *Electric shock between a live part and earth*

The earth fault path

There are a number of ways to provide this return path. In each case the objectives are to:

● allow fault currents to return safely to the supply transformer, and to
● disconnect the supply to the faulty circuit before any danger from fire, shock or burns can occur.

We briefly mentioned the types of systems earlier so let's look at the earthing arrangement for each system in more detail. For clarity we will use a simple single-phase supply circuit for each system which will not include the energy meter, distribution board, consumer unit and so on.

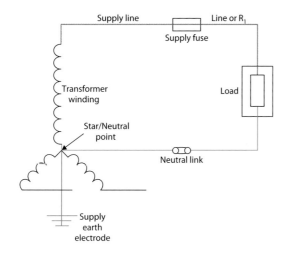

Figure 1.2 *The basic supply circuit with no earthing shown*

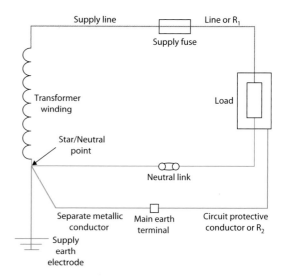

Figure 1.3 *The TN-S earthing arrangement*

A system is a single source of supply and an installation and Figure 1.2 shows the basic circuit taken from a three-phase transformer. We shall consider each earthing system in terms of a single winding of the supply transformer, supply cables between the transformer and the installation, and the installation itself.

As we saw earlier, each type of system earth has a particular classification which we shall use for their identification.

TN-S system

This tells us that:

First letter **T** – the supply is connected directly to earth at one or more points.

Second letter **N** – the exposed metalwork of the installation is connected directly to the earthing point of the supply. (The neutral of the supply system is normally earthed.)

Third letter **S** – a separate conductor is used throughout the system to provide the connection of the exposed conductive parts to the earth of the supply.

This earth connection is usually either through the sheath of the supply cable or a separate conductor

within the supply cable. Separate protective conductors are used within the installation to connect the exposed conductive parts to the main earthing terminal. In the event of a fault to earth in this system the current flow will be around the earth fault loop as shown in Figure 1.4.

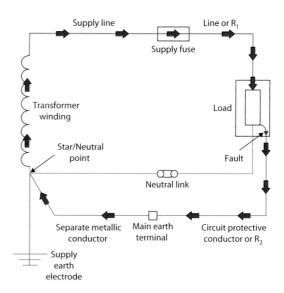

Figure 1.4 *TN-S Earth fault path*

As a conductor is used throughout the whole system to provide a return path for the earth fault current, the return path should have a low value of impedance. The protective conductors are generally a smaller csa than the live conductors.

TN-C-S system

This type of system is similar to the TN-S system except for one important feature as we shall see.

First letter **T** – the supply is connected directly to earth at one or more points.

Second letter **N** – the exposed metalwork of the installation is connected directly to the earthing point of the supply. (The neutral of the supply system is normally earthed.)

Third letter **C** – within the DNO's supply system the function of neutral conductor and earth conductor are combined in a single common conductor known as a protective earth neutral (PEN) conductor.

Fourth letter **S** – a separate conductor must be used throughout the installation to provide the connection of the exposed conductive parts to the main earthing terminal. The use of a combined conductor within the installation is **not** permitted.

Again as electrical conductors are used throughout the system a low earth fault return path impedance should be obtained. In the event of an earth fault on this system the current flow will be around the earth fault loop as shown in Figure 1.5.

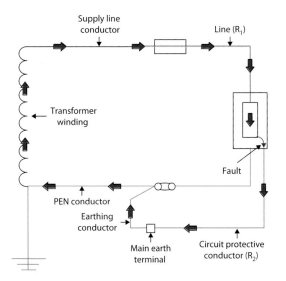

Figure 1.5 *TN-C-S Earth fault path*

TT system

This tells us that:

First letter **T** – the supply is connected directly to earth at one or more points.

Second letter **T** – the installation's exposed metalwork is connected to earth by a separate installation earth electrode.

The connection between these two electrodes, and therefore the return path for earth fault current, is the general mass of earth. When a fault to earth occurs on this system, the earth fault current will flow around the circuit shown in Figure 1.6.

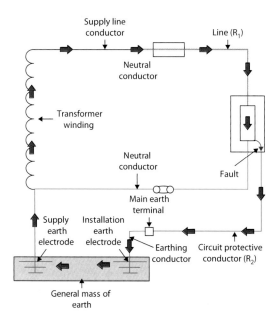

Figure 1.6 *TT Earth fault path*

In this system, the earth fault current returns through the general mass of earth which will generally have a high value of impedance.

The path through which the earth fault current flows is known as the earth fault loop path and the earth fault loop impedance plays a major part in the protection against electric shock.

These three systems are the ones available on the public distribution system. There are two other systems of which we should be aware. These are the TN-C and IT systems which are not available on the public distribution network and are not suitable for general use.

TN-C system

The TN-C earthing arrangement is rarely used and it is one where a combined PEN conductor fulfils both the earthing and neutral functions in both the supply and the installation.

IT system

In the IT system there is either no connection of the supply to earth or the system has only a high impedance connection and an insulation monitoring device monitors the impedance.

As stated earlier, the impedance of the earth fault path plays an important part as it will regulate the amount of current that flows in the event of a fault to earth. This earth fault loop impedance value should be calculated for a proposed installation and measured for a completed installation.

The system earth fault loop impedance (Z_s) comprises the external earth fault loop impedance Z_e which is the DNO's part of the system and the resistance of the line (R_1) and the circuit protective conductor (R_2) of the electrical installation. So $Z_s = Z_e + (R_1 + R_2)$ and we can use these values during the design stage to determine compliance of the proposed installation.

The measurement of the earth fault loop impedance is carried out using a special test instrument and is measured between line and earth. We need a low value of impedance to ensure a good return path to encourage large currents to flow when a fault to earth occurs.

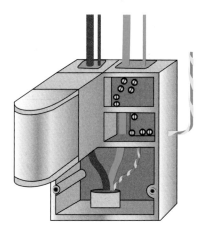

Figure 1.7 *Typical TN-S system domestic intake*

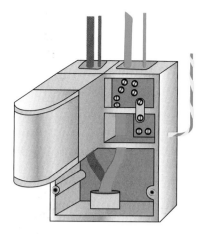

Figure 1.8 *Typical TN-C-S system*

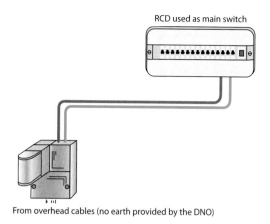

RCD used as main switch

From overhead cables (no earth provided by the DNO)

Figure 1.9 *Typical TT system*

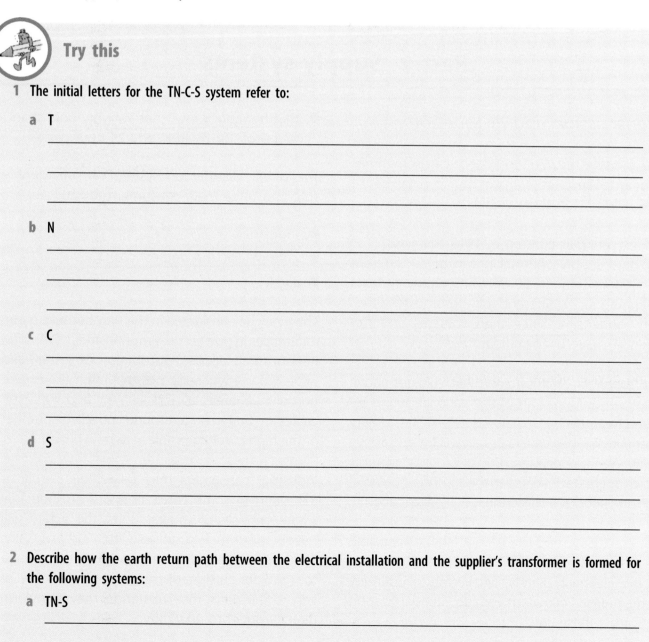

Try this

1 The initial letters for the TN-C-S system refer to:

a T

_____

_____

_____

b N

_____

_____

_____

c C

_____

_____

_____

d S

_____

_____

_____

2 Describe how the earth return path between the electrical installation and the supplier's transformer is formed for the following systems:

a TN-S

_____

_____

_____

b TN-C-S

_____

_____

_____

c TT

_____

_____

_____

Part 2 Supply systems

Transmission and distribution

The modern distribution system can sometimes appear to be quite complex but it is far better than was previously available.

For example, in London in 1919 there were 80 separate supply undertakings with 70 different generating stations, 50 different supply systems operating at 24 different voltages and 10 different frequencies. Since then voltages and frequencies have been standardized.

The supply of electrical energy at voltages above 33kV, which forms part of the National Grid, is referred to as the Transmission Network. The primary distribution system operates below 33kV and above 11kV. We shall consider the distribution systems which operate at 11kV called the secondary distribution and 400/230V called the tertiary distribution.

The electricity suppliers have a legal responsibility to keep the supply within the limits identified in the Electricity Safety, Quality and Continuity Regulations. Following voltage standardization in Europe these are:

- for voltage a nominal supply of 400/230V, + 10%, – 6%

- that frequency must not vary by more than +/-1% of 50Hz within any 24 hour period.

The public distribution system can be roughly split into three main consumer groups:

- industrial
- commercial and domestic
- rural.

They may be considered in this way because of the differences in power consumption and the remoteness of rural supplies. Distribution cables are laid underground wherever possible. With the exception of rural areas, almost all 11kV and 400/230V cables are buried underground and a large number of the higher voltage cables are now buried.

Industrial consumers may take their supply at 33kV and in some cases 132kV. If an industrial estate consists of smaller units, the estate will have a substation supplied with 132kV or 33kV. The transformer will then step-down the voltage to 11kV for further distribution. In the case of very small units the substation may transform directly down to 400/230V.

Large commercial premises may have their own substation transformer fed at 11kV, which will step down the voltage to 400/230V for internal distribution, whilst smaller commercial and domestic consumers are usually supplied at 400/230V.

The 11kV input to the transformer will be connected in delta whereas the 400/230V output will be a star arrangement (Figure 1.11). To supply the delta connected windings a three-phase three-wire system is used, with no neutral conductor. The star connected output uses a three-phase four-wire connection with the centre point of the star being the neutral which is connected to earth.

In delta the voltage across each of the lines (line voltage) is the same as the transformer winding, whereas a transformer winding connected in star will give us a voltage between lines of 400V (U) and a voltage between any line and the neutral star point of 230V (U_o), (Figure 1.11).

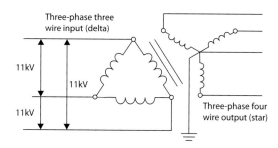

Figure 1.11 *Typical delta/star transformer arrangement*

The number and colour identification of line conductors in the UK is Brown/L1, Black/L2 and Grey/L3 with the neutral Blue/N.

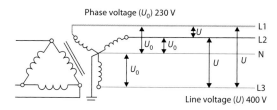

Figure 1.12 *Voltages available from a star connected transformer winding*

Try this

Using Figure 1.10 insert the most appropriate voltage in each of the boxes.

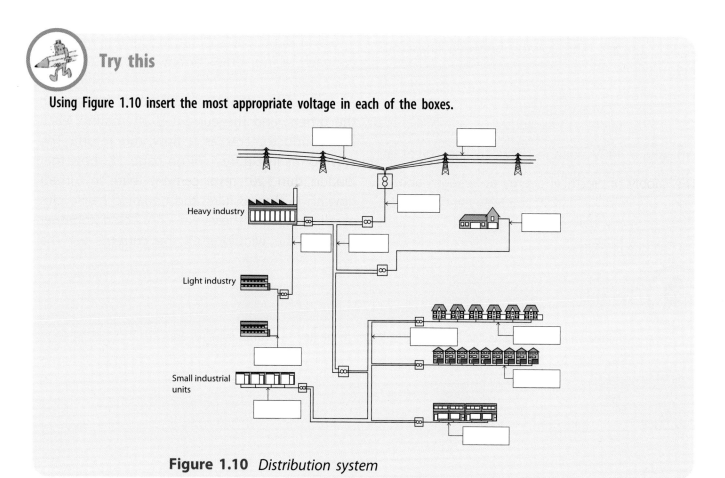

Figure 1.10 *Distribution system*

The relationship between the voltage line to neutral and the voltage line to line voltage for a star connected winding is:

$$\text{Voltage line to neutral} = \frac{\text{Voltage between lines}}{\sqrt{3}}$$

$$\text{Voltage line to line} = \text{Voltage line to neutral} \times \sqrt{3}$$

Where $\sqrt{3}$ = approximately 1.732

Note

The line to line voltage is equal to the sum of the two line to neutral voltages each multiplied by sine 120° (voltages displaced by 120°). The sine of 120° is 0.866 which is equal to half $\sqrt{3}$. As there are two L-N voltages displaced by 120° we have the line to neutral voltage $\times \sqrt{3}$.

Example:

The nominal line to neutral voltage is 230V for most single-phase installations on the public network in the UK. The voltage between lines for this supply is:

$$230 \times \sqrt{3} = 230 \times 1.73$$
$$= 400V$$

Similarly, a 400V voltage between lines gives a voltage line to neutral of:

$$\frac{400}{\sqrt{3}} = \frac{400}{1.73} = 230V$$

Load currents in three-phase circuits

It is important to recognize the relationships of the currents in star and delta connected windings. In star connected the current through the line conductors is equal to that flowing through the phase windings, as shown in Figure 1.13, and so we can see that $I_L = I_P$.

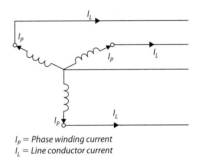

I_P = Phase winding current
I_L = Line conductor current

Figure 1.13 *Current in a star connected load*

However, in the delta connected winding this appears to be more complex. The line current, when reaching the transformer winding, is split into two directions so that two phase windings are each taking some current.

As each of the phases is 120° out of phase with the others, and the current is alternating, each line conductor acts as a flow and return. The waveforms in Figure 1.14 on page 11 show that due to this 120° displacement there is current flowing in the positive and negative half cycles at all times. As these are connected together through the windings all the currents are the

Try this

For star connected windings calculate the line to line voltages if the line to neutral voltages are:

a 415V _____

b 230V _____

c 110V _____

same, the current will effectively cancel each other and so there will be no need for a neutral conductor in a delta connected load.

Remember

In a single-phase system the neutral will carry the load current.

In a star connected three-phase system the neutral conductor will carry the out of balance load current.

In a balanced three-phase system (delta connected) there is no imbalance and so a neutral conductor is not required.

The currents through the phase windings are:

$$I_P = \frac{I_L}{\sqrt{3}}$$

$$\text{or } I_L = I_P \times \sqrt{3}$$

Example:

If the line current is 100A the phase winding current is:

$$I_P = \frac{100}{\sqrt{3}} = \frac{100}{1.73}$$

$$= 57.8A$$

Three-phase balanced loads

All transmission and primary distribution is carried out using a three-phase system. It is important that each of the phases carries about the same amount of current.

Three-phase motors have equal windings and each phase is the same. Therefore the conductors carry the same current, and these automatically create a balanced load situation.

For domestic areas the output of the star connected transformer is 400/230V. All premises are generally supplied with a single-phase and

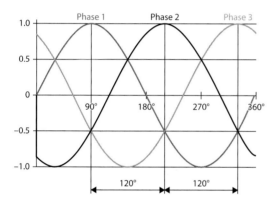

Figure 1.14 *Balanced three-phase current waveform*

For example: At 90° Phase 1 positive = Phase 2 + Phase 3 negative so the arithmetic sum is zero.

Considering what we have learnt about current in a balanced delta system the arrows shown on Figure 1.15 only give an indication as to the current distribution for each line. All of these currents would **not** be flowing in the directions shown at the same time.

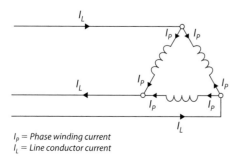

I_P = Phase winding current
I_L = Line conductor current

Figure 1.15 *Current in a delta connected load*

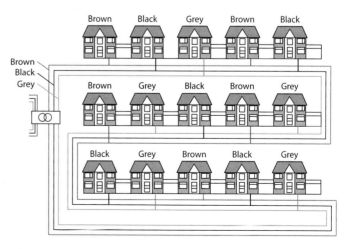

Figure 1.16 *Houses are connected so that their loads are spread across the three phases*

Try this

Describe the function of the neutral conductor in a:

a single-phase circuit _____

b three-phase star circuit _____

c balanced three-phase delta _____

neutral at 230V. To try to balance the loads on each of the phases, houses may be connected as shown in Figure 1.16. If it was possible to load all of the phases exactly the same the current in the neutral would be zero.

The distribution of electrical energy is tailored to the needs and location of the consumer in relation to the supply source. The use of transformers to determine the distribution system voltage allows the supplier to size cables and control gear to give maximum network efficiency and convenience to the customer. When the supply enters the consumer's premises, connection is made to the customer's own distribution system and final circuits. These systems and circuits will vary depending on the type of consumer, the energy requirement and the type of equipment being used, so we shall consider typical final circuit arrangements for the most common groups of consumers.

Domestic

Domestic consumers generally receive their supply at 230V, single-phase, from the supply company, although in areas where electric space heating is employed a second or third phase may be supplied. This is because, depending on the size of the heating load, it may be necessary to distribute the current demand across the phases.

The final distribution circuits for the domestic installation, lighting and power circuits, operate at 230V, single-phase throughout. Some items of equipment, for specific locations or in order to provide specialist control or effects, are supplied at a lower voltage. These items of equipment will generally operate at extra low voltage, below 50V ac, and are supplied via their own local transformer.

Figure 1.17 *SELV lighting in a kitchen*

Each final circuit must be controlled by a protective device suitably rated to supply the load of the circuit which it protects. The requirements for the protection of the final circuits are covered later in this chapter. Each final circuit must have its own protective device and the distribution board in domestic installations is generally a consumer unit containing miniature circuit breakers or fuses. Other protective devices, such as residual current devices may also be incorporated and again these will be considered later in this study guide.

A typical domestic consumer unit is shown in Figure 1.18, and the rating of the devices will vary between say a 6A device for the protection of the lighting circuits through to 45A devices for the larger power using equipment such as large electric showers and cookers.

Figure 1.18 *Typical (Dual RCD) domestic consumer unit*

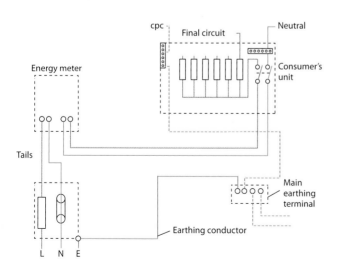

Figure 1.19 *Typical TN-S domestic schematic diagram*

Commercial

The arrangement of final circuits in small commercial premises may be very similar to that of the domestic installation. However, larger commercial buildings will have a considerably bigger floor area and a greater power requirement. The same consideration needs to be given to the economic use of conductor sizes and effective utilization of equipment within the consumer's installation as is given to the supply network.

As a result it is common to install distribution circuits within the installation. In a multi-storey building, for example, a distribution circuit may be installed to each floor. These would generally comprise a means of isolation and protection at the intake position, a large cross-sectional area cable to a convenient point on the appropriate floor and a distribution board containing the final circuit protection devices for the circuits on that level.

It is common to try to locate these distribution boards as close to the centre of the area as possible in order to minimize the length of the

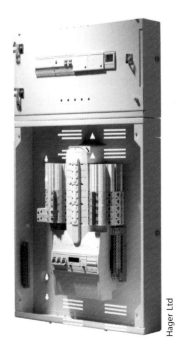

Figure 1.20 *Typical commercial distribution board*

final circuit cables. It is common for the consumer's distribution circuit to be at 400V, three-phase and neutral with the lighting and power circuits for the floor area being supplied at 230V single-phase. Again special areas, or the requirement for sophisticated controls, may require extra low voltage systems to be installed.

Remember that a similar approach may be taken to a single storey building which covers a large floor area with the distribution boards being placed at convenient locations around the building. These are often referred to as power centres.

three-phase equipment. It is quite common to find that the general lighting and power in such installations are at 230V single-phase and that 400V three-phase final circuits are installed to supply particular items of equipment such as motors.

Figure 1.22 *Large three-phase industrial system*

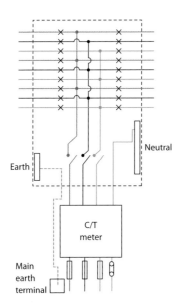

Figure 1.21 *Schematic layout for a commercial installation*

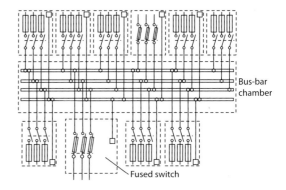

Figure 1.23 *Circuit diagram for a three-phase distribution system*

Industrial

Small industrial units will often receive their supply at 400/230V from the supply company and their final circuit arrangements may be very similar to those of the commercial installation above.

Many industrial applications involve the use of equipment with a high power requirement, which is often achieved most economically with

Industrial installations with a high energy demand may take their supply at high voltage (11 or 33kV), with much higher demands having supplies at 132kV and above. Where the supply is at 11kV or above consumers will need to provide their own substation transformer and distribution equipment. There will also be a need for the consumer to engage suitably qualified and competent engineers to maintain their system. Loss of even a part of the system could seriously disrupt the consumer's activities.

In essence the consumer's distribution network can, for our purposes, be regarded as being similar to that of the supply company. The consumer's network is used to economically provide an electrical supply to the parts of the installation where it is required. In some instances the consumer may have equipment which operates at voltages in excess of 400V three-phase, but we shall not consider those here.

Having been distributed through the consumer's own network and transformer(s) the supply for each area is derived from an intake position within the consumer's premises. This may be further distributed as in the commercial and smaller industrial installations described above.

Agricultural

Agricultural installations are generally located in remote areas, surrounded by agricultural land. As a result they are often some distance from the supply company's distribution network. It is common for such installations to be supplied via an overhead line network as the cost of burying supply cables over the distances involved is uneconomic.

It is usually economical for the supply company to install a pole-mounted transformer locally to supply the installation, thus reducing the losses on the supply network. Farm installations often receive their supply at 400/230V and this is then distributed to the farm buildings, often by the use of overhead conductors. The general lighting and power will be at 230V single-phase but, as with the smaller industrial equipment, many of the items of machinery will require 400V three-phase supplies.

Figure 1.24 *Typical cattle shed*

Each of the types of installation already mentioned will have its own unique requirements and it is not possible to consider them all here. We can however generalize on the requirements for the different types of final circuit and consider typical applications. We can categorize the basic final circuits into some specific areas and consider the requirements for each.

Heating

Final circuits in this category will include those supplying space heating, water heating and cooking applications. As a general rule these final circuits will be supplying equipment which will draw considerable current, and require large cross-sectional area cables to deliver it. By supplying such circuits at voltages greater than 230V single-phase, 50Hz, the current required to produce the same power output can be considerably reduced. In domestic premises it is often not practical nor cost effective to supply this equipment at above 230V.

As a result these circuits generally require the largest cables. Installations which receive their supply at 400V and above will benefit from supplying their large heating loads at 400V three-phase and above.

> **Note**
>
> More information on the calculation of three-phase power is contained in the study guide *Principles of Design, Installation and Maintenance* in this series.

Power

General power outlets are provided at 230V and these are common to most installations. The type of outlet may vary dependent upon the type of equipment and the intended use of the circuit, but the BS 1363, 13A socket outlet appears in almost every installation. Larger equipment which requires more power will be supplied by a dedicated final circuit. Some industrial applications require the installation of 400V, three-phase or three-phase and neutral socket outlets. These are often used to supply portable or transportable equipment which would otherwise require a much larger single-phase circuit.

Lighting

Lighting is generally supplied at 230V single-phase, and the type of lamp used determines the light output, with specialist lamps being employed for applications such as street lighting, car parks and sports halls. Some applications require the lighting to be supplied at extra low voltage (ELV) and some locations may require this to be separated extra low voltage (SELV). Both of these operate at no more than 50V ac.

The difference between them being that the SELV is supplied through a safety isolating transformer to BS EN 61558-2-6.

Figure 1.25 *Street lighting*

Control circuits

Many electrical installations now include equipment which requires sophisticated control circuitry. The domestic dimmer switch, operating at 230V, 50Hz is perhaps one of the most basic controls. Industrial and commercial installations use equipment which often requires an elaborate control system. The commercial installation may require controls on air conditioning and heating systems and there may also be a need for environmental control within an installation. Many companies now use energy management systems which monitor and control all aspects of energy consumption. These systems, whilst seemingly expensive, can in the longer term offer considerable cost savings for the company. The industrial consumer will often require complex control over the production process resulting in considerable savings in both manpower and reduced wastage.

These control systems often involve the use of microprocessors and logic controls, and whilst the equipment being controlled may have a large power consumption, the actual control processes require minute power levels. The current requirements are very low and as a result the use of extra low voltage equipment in electronics is most suitable.

With voltages as low as 12V ac or dc and the small current requirement means that small cables can be used for the interconnection of the control devices. Control circuits are generally supplied via panel-mounted transformers, for the ac devices, or transformer rectifiers for the dc equipment. The control circuits are often supplied through special devices to prevent fluctuations in the supply or interference from the supply system interfering with the control system.

Alarm systems

Alarm systems also operate on very small power requirements, as they basically rely on a change of state in an electronic circuit to cause the operation of an alarm. The majority of systems use electronic equipment throughout and, like

our control systems, operate at voltages as low as 12V.

Many systems are available, some operating on ac and some on dc. Generally the supply to the system is derived from a 230V ac supply and the equipment transforms and rectifies this to provide the extra low voltage for the alarm system. Many alarms operate through internal supplies which incorporate a device allowing the system to be supplied from a separate, usually self-contained, dc source. This source, normally a battery, is maintained in a fully charged state by the main supply. However, in the event of a main supply failure the battery is able to take over and run the system.

Figure 1.26 *Domestic alarm control panel*

Try this

1 List four typical voltages that may be found in an electrical installation within an industrial unit which is in the manufacturing industry, stating their use in each case.

a _____

b _____

c _____

d _____

> **2** State the typical supply voltages for each of the following installations:
>
> **a** Large industrial premises _____
>
> **b** A commercial premises _____
>
> **c** A domestic dwelling _____

Part 3 Protection

The main requirements

There are a number of requirements that must be considered when dealing with control and protection of an installation, the main ones being:

- isolation and switching
- protection against overcurrent
- earth fault protection.

All these requirements are related to safety and need to be considered for protection, not just from electric shock, but also from fire, burns or injury from mechanical movement of equipment which is electrically activated.

Isolation and switching

The term isolation, within this context, means the cutting off of the installation, or circuit, from all sources of electrical supply to prevent danger. In a domestic installation the main means of isolation is usually the main switch controlling the consumer unit.

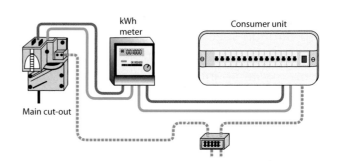

Figure 1.27 *The main intake position of a domestic installation*

Within the installation other local methods are used and the positioning and type of these can be very important.

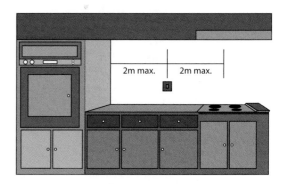

Figure 1.28 *Cooker isolation*

The control for cookers is a double pole switch which should be positioned no further than 2m from the cooker or, as in Figure 1.28, from either part of the cooker as identified in IET Guidance Note 1. We use similar isolation arrangements for immersion heaters and domestic boilers and the like.

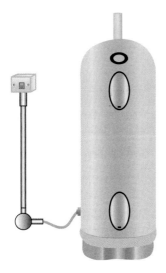

Figure 1.29 *Immersion heaters must have a double pole control switch adjacent to the heater*

Figure 1.30 *Domestic boilers often have a plug and socket as the means of isolation*

In an industrial installation the requirements can become far more complex. Whilst within a domestic installation most isolators are double-pole types, in industrial situations there will not only be double pole isolators there will also be triple-pole and triple-pole and neutral (TP&N).

Some examples of the use of isolators in industrial installations are shown in Figure 1.32 and 1.33. Figure 1.34 is an example of emergency switching.

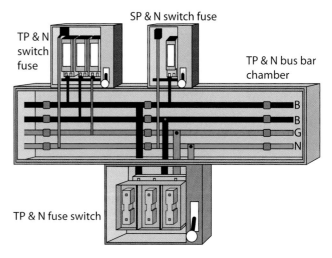

Figure 1.31 *Industrial distribution*

Figure 1.32 *Three-phase distribution board controlled by an isolator*

Figure 1.33 *Motor with an adjacent isolator*

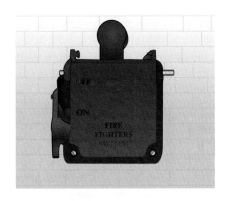

Figure 1.34 *Firefighter's emergency switch*

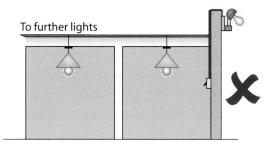

Figure 1.35 *A radial circuit with 10 existing lights has a 500W tungsten halogen lamp added which increases the load to exceed the circuit capacity*

Remember

An isolator must cut off an electrical installation, or part of it, from every source of electrical energy.

Overcurrent protection

Overload

An overload is a situation that occurs in a circuit which is still electrically sound. It is generally caused by trying to take more power from a circuit than it is designed for, which results in a larger than normal current flowing in the circuit. If the load is reduced then the circuit can continue to function without any need for repair.

A typical example of this is a radial circuit which has been extended and the load has increased to exceed that originally intended. Each item connected in the circuit and the circuit supplying the equipment is healthy but more current is being drawn through the cable than was originally intended.

Every cable has some resistance, and the result of drawing more current through the cable is the production of more heat in the cable. This rise in temperature will, over a period of time, result in the insulation becoming less effective and eventually breaking down. In the case of severe overload the insulation becomes so hot it begins to melt and may even catch fire. This is obviously a serious fire risk and we must take steps to prevent this happening.

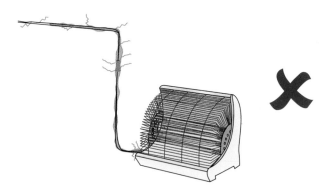

Figure 1.36 *Severe overload creates a real fire risk*

Adding load to a circuit over time, such as plugging in additional equipment to a socket outlet circuit, can result in a gradual increase in load current which may continue for some time before the protective device disconnects from the supply. So an overload can be a gradual increase in current.

Try this

1 Explain how a circuit may become overloaded.

_____

_____

2 Explain how an overloaded cable could cause a fire.

_____

_____

Short circuit

A short, unlike an overload, is the connecting together of live conductors which results in a very rapid increase in current, in nanoseconds. This produces a very high current in the circuit, as the only impedance in the circuit is that of the electrical conductors and this is very low. The protective device has to be able to safely disconnect the potential current that would flow in the case of a short circuit, and this may be in thousands of amperes.

Part 4 Earth fault protection

Earth fault protection is designed to protect against electric shock, fire and burns as a result of a fault to earth. This will result in all the exposed and extraneous conductive parts within the installation becoming live.

The installation we are considering is part of a TN-S system and the installation is connected to the supply transformer with line and neutral conductors and the earth is provided by the supply cable sheath.

An appliance, in this case an electric kettle, is plugged into a socket outlet. The element will be connected between line and neutral to make it work normally, and the metal case will be connected to the earth pin of the plug. Under normal operating conditions no current would flow in the earthed conductor.

However, if a fault develops, such as corrosion of the element's outer cover, resulting in current leaking from the live element through the water to the metal case of the kettle, then the case of the kettle becomes live. This creates a real risk of electric shock and the kettle must be disconnected before it can create a danger.

As the metal case of the kettle is connected to earth, the fault current will flow through the earth return path and back to the earthed point of the supply transformer. There has to be a complete circuit for current to flow. By creating a low impedance return path using good

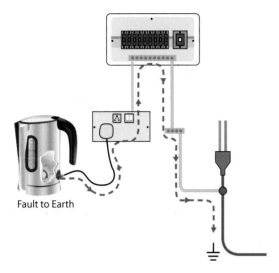

Figure 1.37 *Fault to earth on an electric kettle*

electrical conductors a complete circuit for the return of the earth fault current to the source transformer is provided.

Remember

We are using impedance for the earth fault loop circuit because it is an ac current which will flow in the circuit.

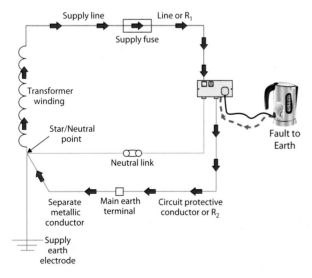

Figure 1.38 *Fault path in the TN-S system*

It is important that the impedance of the earth fault path is kept as low as possible so that in the event of an earth fault the maximum current can flow. We need this high current to flow in order to operate the protective device and disconnect the supply.

There are two significant requirements here:

1 the fault is disconnected from the supply
2 the disconnection is fast enough to prevent a fatal electric shock occurring.

If the earth fault path has a high enough impedance the current may continue to flow without the protective device operating.

Remember

The I_n (current rating) of a protective device is the current it can carry for an indefinite time without deterioration.

For a protective device to operate current in excess of the I_n rating must flow. For example: a 32A BS 88-3 type fuse will take around 140A to cause the fuse to disconnect in 5 seconds and 240A to disconnect in 0.4 seconds. For final circuits rated up to and including ($\leq$) 32A BS 7671 requires a disconnection time of 0.4 seconds to provide fault protection.

We can see from this that if only a small earth fault current occurs, due to the high earth fault path impedance, then the protective device will not operate in time.

A current of around 50mA (0.05A) is sufficient to cause ventricular fibrillation of the heart for the average person, which can result in death. So if a fault current of 50mA flows to earth on a circuit protected by a protective device rated at, say, 10A the current in the line conductor is only 10A + 50mA, a total of 10.05A and this will not cause the protection device to operate.

It is important to remember that the human body can be affected by currents as low as 5mA. If the fault path passes through the human body there is a risk of electric shock even at these very low current levels.

Note

Appendix 3 of BS 7671 contains time current curves for protective devices and each set of curves contains an inset table which indicates the current required for the protective device to operate within given times.

Earth fault impedance test

To ensure that this earth fault path has a low enough earth fault impedance an earth fault loop impedance test is carried out. This test passes a current through the earth return path from the premises to the supply transformer, through the windings and back to the consumer's premises through the line conductor.

There are two tests involving earth fault loop impedance:

- Z_e – the earth fault loop impedance of the earth return path external to the installation (the supplier's part of the system)
- Z_s – the earth fault impedance of the whole system (the external path and the line and cpc conductors of the circuit)

Z_e is measured at the origin of the installation with the installation isolated from the supply and all parallel paths disconnected. This is normally done by disconnecting the earthing conductor from the main earthing terminal, hence the need for the installation to be isolated from the supply.

Z_s is carried out at the furthest point of all radial circuits (the point of maximum impedance for the earth fault loop path). The test is also carried out at all accessible socket outlets on ring final circuits.

Task

Determine, using the information contained in Appendix 3 of BS 7671, the current required to cause each of the following protective devices to operate within the time given:

a   20A, BS 88-3 fuse system C, in 0.4 seconds _____

b   30A, BS3036 semi-enclosed fuse, in 0.2 seconds _____

c   80A, BS 88-2 fuse system E, in 5 seconds _____

d   32A, BS EN 60898 type B circuit breaker in 0.4 seconds _____

Note

There is more information on testing, including testing earth fault loop impedance in the study guide *Inspection, Testing and Commissioning* in this series.

Remember

If the earthing arrangement for an installation becomes disconnected, exposed metalwork of the installation (exposed conductive parts) and metalwork of other services and the building structure (extraneous conductive parts) may become live and reach the supply voltage U_0 of 230V.

Try this

1 Explain why a low earth fault loop impedance is necessary to provide fault protection.

_____

_____

_____

_____

_____

_____

_____

2 Using the information in this chapter list all the component parts of the earth fault loop impedance path in a TN-C-S system starting at the point of fault:

_____

_____

_____

_____

_____

_____

_____

_____

Try this: Crossword

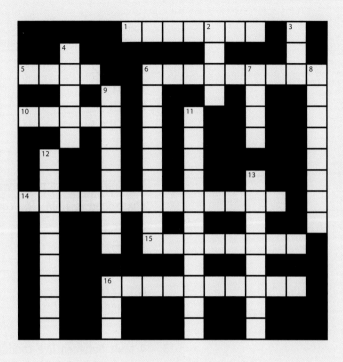

Across

1   Out in the cold or a steel trunking is this type of conductive part. (7)

5   The three-phase load connection for unbalanced loads. (4)

6   Required for safety when working on a circuit. (9)

10 The three-phase load connection for balanced loads. (5)

14 Safe removal from all sources of supply. (13)

15 The principle requirement for fault protection. (8)

16 Fuses and circuit breakers may provide this. (10)

Down

2   A 25V supply from an isolating transformer initially. (4)

3   Responsible for maintaining the supply equipment to the installation. (3)

4   When current flows outside the intended path it produces this. (5)

6   AC resistance? (9)

7   This distribution system includes a PEN conductor. (4)

8   The opposite to 13 down. (8)

9   A sine...... is pictorial demonstration of an AC current. (8)

11 Both overload and short circuit are this. (11)

12 Part of the control measures for electrical installations. (9)

13 A 'can do' attitude is this. (8)

16 A version of 7 down. (3)

Congratulations, you have completed Chapter 1 of this study guide. Complete the self assessment questions before progressing to Chapter 2.

SELF ASSESSMENT

1   The type of supply system which uses a PEN conductor to connect the main earthing terminal to the supply transformer is:

a.   TT

b.   TN-S

c.   TN-C-S

d.   IT

2   The current in the phase winding of a large three-phase load is 160A. The current in the line conductor will be:

a.   92A

b.   53A

c.   227A

d.   480A

3   A fault between live conductors will result in:

a.   overload

b.   short circuit

c.   earth leakage currents

d.   no change in circuit conditions

4   To cause the fuse in a domestic immersion heater circuit to operate when a fault to earth occurs, the current which flows in the earth path must be a:

a.   high DC current

b.   low DC current

c.   high AC current

d.   low AC current

5   Z_e represents the earth fault loop impedance that is:

a.   external to the installation

b.   for the complete system

c.   within the installation

d.   for a single circuit

Earthing arrangements

RECAP

Before you start work on this chapter, complete the exercise below to ensure that you remember what you learned earlier.

- The total path taken by earth fault currents is called the earth fault loop _____ and the impedance of this path must be _____ to provide _____ protection.

- The connection between the main earthing _____ and the DNOs transformer for a TN-C-S system is the _____ conductor and for a _____ it is the general mass of earth.

- The supply of electrical energy at voltages above 33kV is referred to as the _____ network. Primary distribution is the system which operates at between _____kV and _____kV. Secondary distribution is the system which operates at _____kV. Tertiary distribution is the system which operates at 400/_____V.

- In a balanced three-phase load the _____ flowing in the neutral conductor will be _____.

- The final circuit for domestic installation, lighting and power circuits, operates at _____V, _____.

- If the voltage between line conductors of a three-phase star connected load is 400V the voltage across each phase winding will be _____V _____ by $\sqrt{3}$.

- If the current in each phase winding of a delta connected load is 25A the current in the line conductor will be _____A multiplied by $\sqrt{3}$.

- A fault between _____ conductors produces a _____ circuit whilst an increase in load in a healthy circuit is an _____.

LEARNING OBJECTIVES

This chapter considers the earthing arrangements for electrical installations both within and external to buildings and structures. You will need to refer to BS 7671 and IET Guidance Note 1 when you are working through this chapter. You may also find the IET On-Site Guide helpful.

On completion of this chapter you should be able to:

● Explain the principles of earthing and bonding.

● Explain the protection of electrical systems including:

  – automatic disconnection

  – basic principles of shock protection

  – circuit overload and short-circuit protection in terms of maximum disconnection times

  – discrimination between protective devices

  – fault current capacities of devices

● Explain the operating principles, applications and limitations of protective devices.

● State what is meant by earth fault loop impedance and protective multiple earthing (PME).

Part 1 Earthing and bonding

Earthing and bonding

The terms earthing and bonding refer to two distinctly different functions, both of which are essential where Automatic Disconnection of Supply (ADS) is the method to provide protection against electric shock. As ADS is by far the most common method of fault protection used in electrical installations it is important that we understand the difference between the functions of earthing and bonding.

The mutual association of earthing and bonding has resulted in the misuse and misunderstanding of these terms and their function so we will look at each separately and then see how they relate to each other.

Task

Using BS 7671, look up the definitions of an exposed conductive part and an extraneous conductive part.

Earthing

There are three functions performed by earthing:

● Connecting all exposed conductive parts of the electrical installation to the main earth terminal and to the source earth.

● Maintaining all the exposed conductive parts in the installation at substantially the same potential at all times (normal operation and earth fault conditions).

● Providing a low resistance return path for earth fault currents.

To distribution boards

Main protective bonding conductors

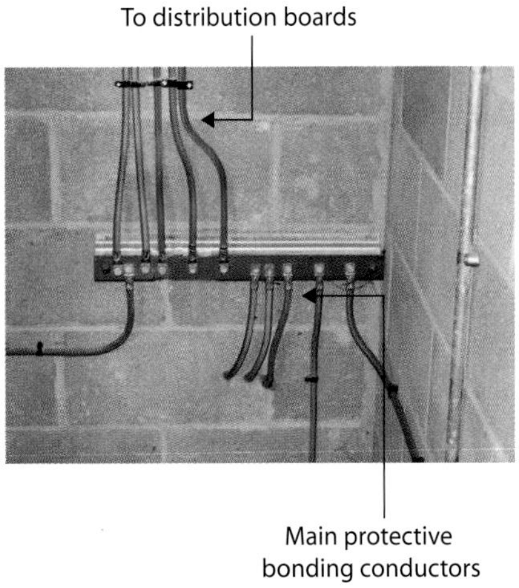

Figure 2.1 *Industrial installation main earthing terminal*

> ### Remember
> **Exposed conductive parts are parts of the electrical installation which are conductive and can be touched. This includes such things as the cases of cookers and fridges, steel conduit and trunking and metal accessories such as switches and luminaires.**

As all the exposed conductive parts are connected together they will all be substantially at the same potential at all times. Should a fault to earth occur anywhere on the installation all the exposed conductive parts will become live, up to a potential of 230V ac rms, until such time as the fault is disconnected from the supply.

We saw in Chapter 1 that as part of the earth fault loop impedance path the main earthing terminal is connected to the source earth.

However, as all the exposed conductive parts are at substantially the same potential, the risk of electric shock to someone touching two exposed conductive parts simultaneously is negligible.

> ### Note
> **BS 7671 requires that** *'A circuit protective conductor shall be run to and terminated at each point in the wiring and at each accessory except a lampholder having no exposed-conductive-parts suspended from such a point'.* **This is regardless of whether there are any exposed conductive parts present at each point.**

> ### Remember
> **A potential difference is necessary to produce a current flow. If the exposed conductive parts are at the same potential then there will be no potential difference between them and so no current will flow through the body.**

Circuit protective conductors are used within the electrical installation to connect each exposed conductive part of each circuit to the main earthing terminal. As a result, all the exposed conductive parts are connected together at the main earthing terminal, and so to the source earth.

So the circuit protective conductors keep all the exposed conductive parts at substantially the same potential by connecting them to the main earthing terminal and each other. This also forms part of the low resistance earth path we need to provide earth fault protection by ADS.

Bonding

There are two types of bonding:

- main protective bonding
- supplementary equipotential bonding.

Main protective bonding

We have established that the earthing within the installation maintains the exposed conductive parts at substantially the same potential. However, any extraneous conductive parts will not be at the same potential as the exposed conductive parts. As a result, simultaneous contact between exposed and extraneous conductive parts could result in an electric shock.

Structural steelwork

Figure 2.2 *Electric shock between an exposed and extraneous conductive part*

Remember

BS 7671 defines an extraneous conductive part as *'A conductive part liable to introduce a potential, generally earth potential, and not forming part of the electrical installation'.*

Main protective bonding conductors are used to connect the extraneous conductive parts to the main earthing terminal. These conductors ensure that the exposed and extraneous conductive parts within the installation are all at substantially the same potential. The risk of electric shock due to simultaneous contact between exposed and extraneous conductive parts is considerably reduced.

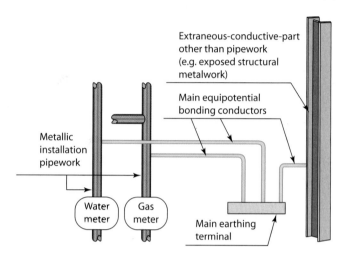

Extraneous-conductive-part other than pipework (e.g. exposed structural metalwork)

Main equipotential bonding conductors

Metallic installation pipework

Water meter

Gas meter

Main earthing terminal

Figure 2.3 *Main protective bonding conductor connections*

This connecting of the exposed and extraneous conductive parts to the main earthing terminal creates an equipotential zone where all the exposed and extraneous conductive parts are connected together and at substantially the same potential. This considerably reduces the risk of electric shock within the installation.

Supplementary equipotential bonding

Supplementary bonding is primarily used in two ways:

- in areas of increased shock risk
- where a sufficiently low enough earth fault loop impedance cannot be achieved.

In areas of increased shock risk, such as locations containing a bath or shower, swimming pools and locations where livestock are housed, the susceptibility of humans and livestock to electric shock is increased. This is often due to the environmental conditions and a reduction in contact resistance between bodies and conductive parts.

Where this is the case, supplementary bonding is installed to further reduce the risk of electric shock. Unlike main protective bonding this does not connect to the main earthing terminal. All the exposed and extraneous conductive parts in the area of increased risk are connected together by a supplementary bonding conductor. This maintains them at the same potential which further reduces the risk of electric shock.

Due to conductor resistance and resistance of the extraneous conductive parts between the MET and the increased shock risk location there may be a difference of potential between the conductive parts.

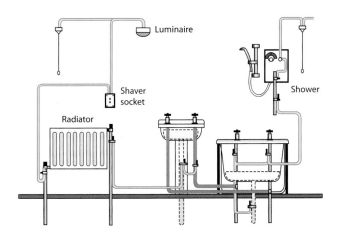

Figure 2.4 *Supplementary bonding in a bathroom*

For example, in a location containing an electric shower there are two circuits, the electric shower and the lighting. The electric shower has a cpc of $4mm^2$ csa and is routed directly from the distribution board to the shower, a distance of, say, 15m. The lighting by contrast is the last light on the lighting circuit and the cpc is $1.0mm^2$ csa with a total length to the light of 35m. If the

resistance of these conductors is calculated we find $10m \times .00461\Omega = 0.0461\Omega$ for the shower and $35 \times 0.0181\Omega = 0.63\Omega$ for the lighting, so the lighting cpc has almost 14 times the resistance of the shower cpc. If 230V appears at the MET as the result of a fault then the potential of the exposed conductive parts at the light and the shower will not be the same. Connecting a supplementary bonding conductor between the shower and the lighting circuit earth terminals in the location equalizes the potential on each and further reduces the risk of electric shock.

Where a suitably low earth fault loop impedance cannot be achieved then the most common action is to install a residual current device (RCD) for additional protection. However, this is not always a suitable solution and in such cases supplementary bonding may be installed to include the circuit and any simultaneously accessible exposed or extraneous conductive parts. Again this maintains all the exposed and extraneous conductive parts at the same potential and, coincidentally, provides a reduced impedance due to the parallel paths it introduces. This reduces the risk of electric shock during the time taken for the circuit to be disconnected from the supply.

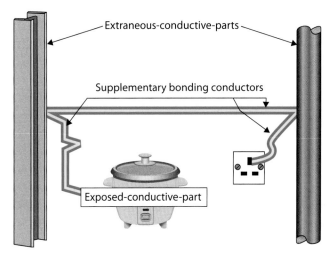

Figure 2.5 *Supplementary bonding where earth loop impedance is too high*

Task

BS 7671 requires a warning label to be placed at every connection of a bonding conductor to an extraneous conductive part. Using the information in Chapter 51 of BS 7671 fill in the required wording in the label.

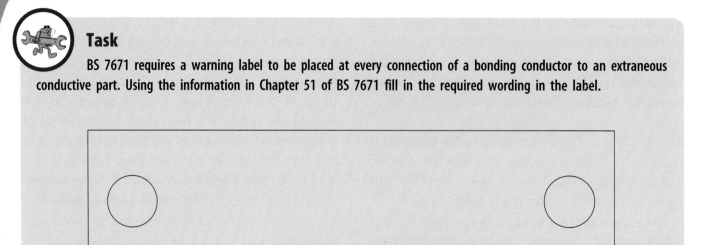

Part 2 Disconnection times

In Chapter 1 we considered the need for a low earth return path and that this is linked to the disconnection time of the protective device in the event of a fault to earth. This disconnection time is dependent upon the type of circuit which is involved. BS 7671 requires disconnection times based upon the circuit use, the nominal voltage U_0 and the type of system.

The most common nominal voltage to earth in the systems available on the public distribution system is 230V and so we shall consider circuits operating at this voltage for this exercise.

For ac final circuits up to and including 32A and operating at U_0 of 230 volts, the maximum disconnection times are:

- TN systems: 0.4 seconds
- TT systems: 0.2 seconds.

For ac distribution circuits and final circuits rated above 32A operating at U_0 of 230V, the maximum disconnection times are:

- TN systems: 5.0 seconds
- TT systems: 2.0 seconds.

In order to achieve these disconnection times the earth fault loop impedance of the circuit(s) must be low enough to cause the protective device to operate in the time required.

To better understand the role the earth fault loop path plays we need to consider the current that needs to flow for the protective device to disconnect within the time.

Remember

The rating of the protective device I_n is the current it can carry for an indefinite period without undue deterioration.

As the rated current of the protective device is the current it can carry without deterioration it follows that we need more current than I_n to flow to achieve disconnection. The amount of current that is required depends upon the type of device and the disconnection time required.

Appendix 3 of BS 7671 contains time current curves for the various types of protective devices. Inset with these graphs is a table for each type of device identifying the current required to cause disconnection within specified times.

If we consider a BS 88-2 systems E&G fuse rated at 32A we can see that the fault currents required are given in Table 2.1.

Table 2.1 *Maximum time current characteristics for fuses to BS 88-2 systems E&G*

Fuse rating	Current for time				
	0.1 sec	0.2 sec	0.4 sec	1 sec	5 sec
32A	310A	260A	220A	180A	125A

We can see from the figures in Table 2.1 that even at the longest disconnection time a current almost $4 \times I_n$ is needed to disconnect in 5 seconds and almost $7 \times I_n$ for a 0.4 second disconnection time.

If we apply Ohm's Law to these values for a 0.4 second disconnection time and a U_0 of 230V we get:

$$R = \frac{V}{I} = \frac{230}{220} = 1.045\Omega$$

So an earth fault loop impedance of 1.045Ω would ensure disconnection within 0.4 seconds.

In Chapter 41 of BS 7671 are tables which provide the maximum earth fault loop impedances for protective devices to achieve disconnection within the required times. If we refer to Table 41.2 in BS 7671, we find the maximum earth fault loop impedance for a 32A, BS 88-2 system E&G fuse is 1.04Ω.

We established in Chapter 1 that the earth fault loop path, $Z_s = Z_e + (R_1 + R_2)$ and for the public distribution network the maximum declared values of Z_e given by the DNO for the systems are:

- TN-S = 0.8Ω
- TN-C-S = 0.35Ω.

The TT system relies upon the general mass of earth for the return path and so the DNO cannot provide a declared value for this system.

The remainder of the earth fault loop path is made up of the line and cpc conductors within the installation.

The values of earth fault loop impedance we calculated and those given in the tables in BS 7671 are the maximum values. These are the values which must not be exceeded when the circuit is operating. This means that these are the maximum values when the conductors are at their normal operating temperature. We shall consider the implications of this later in this study guide.

Task

Before continuing with this chapter go to BS 7671, Appendix 3, and familiarize yourself with the currents required for the various devices to disconnect within the times required.

We can use a fuse or circuit breaker to provide protection against earth fault currents providing the disconnection times can be achieved. For TT systems the earth fault loop impedance is generally much higher than for the TN systems.

We can see from the information above that for a 32A BS 88-2 system E & G fuse to provide this protection we need an earth fault loop impedance no higher than 1.045Ω. This is normally unachievable for a TT system where earth electrode resistances could be as high as 200Ω. In such instances a residual current device (RCD) is used to ensure disconnection within the required time.

The disconnection time for an RCD is determined by the product standard for the device and for BS EN 61008 and BS EN 61009 RCDs operation must be within 300ms (0.3s) when tested at their operating current, I_n.

Task

Before continuing with this chapter go to BS 7671, Tables 41.2, 41.3 and 41.4 and familiarize yourself with the maximum earth fault loop impedances for the different types of devices to disconnect within 0.4s and 5s.

Part 3 Circuit overload and short-circuit protection

Overload and short circuit

Fuse and circuit breakers are used to provide protection against overload and short circuit currents. In the previous chapter we determined that:

- an overload occurs in a healthy circuit and current often builds up over time
- a short circuit occurs quickly and causes a high current to flow.

The time it takes for a device to disconnect in the event of an overcurrent will depend upon two main factors:

- the characteristics of the device
- the current flow through the device.

For the purpose of this exercise we shall consider the typical characteristics of the types of device used to provide protection against overcurrent. These are generally provided in the form of a graph showing the relationship between operating time and current flow and are referred to as time/current characteristics. Generic (non-specific) versions of these time current characteristics are given in Appendix 3 of BS 7671. More specific details can be obtained from the manufacturers of the particular device to be installed.

We reviewed the current and time required for devices to operate within the required times from the inset tables in Appendix 3 earlier. The time current curves give an indication of the time taken for a device to operate when a particular current flows.

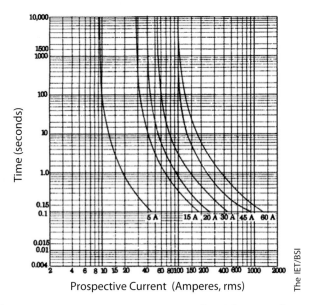

Figure 2.6 *Time current curves for BS 3036 fuses*

current flow increases. For this 20A device the graph provides disconnection times of:

- 20A the value is off the graph as it is I_n for the device
- 40A at 10,000s
- 50A at 20s
- 60A at 5s.

From this we can see that an overload will cause the device to operate but low values of overcurrent will remain for some time. We need at least three times the I_n current to cause operation within 5 s.

If we refer to the time current curve for a 20A BS3036 fuse in Appendix 3 of BS 7671, we can see that the device operates quicker as the

If we look at the time current curves for the other types of fuses, BS 88-2 and BS 88-3, we can see that they all form similar curves but they tend to be steeper and straighter curves depending on the type of fuse. All protective devices will have

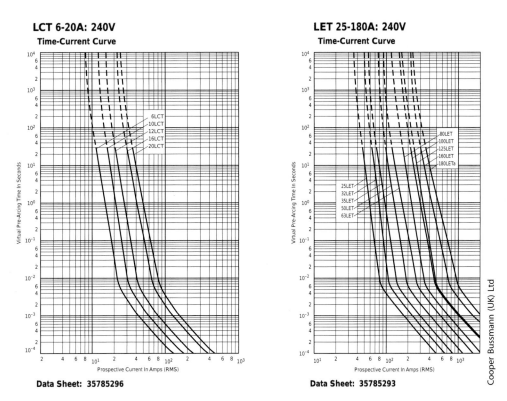

Figure 2.7 *Time current curves for BS 88 fuses from Cooper Bussman*

similar characteristics where small overload currents may continue for some time before disconnection.

The time current curves for BS EN 60898 circuit breakers are a different shape to those of the fuses and we shall consider those in a little more detail and look at the application of the different types.

The first thing to consider is the shape of the curve which is curved at the start (towards I_n for each device) until they reach the 5s point when they become a vertical line. This characteristic is due to the construction of the circuit breaker.

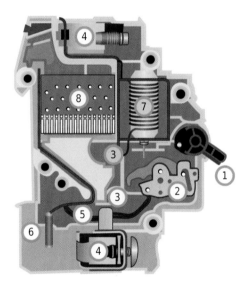

Figure 2.8 *Typical circuit breaker construction*

The thermal part of the circuit breaker, generally a bi-metal link (item 3 in Figure 2.8), is designed to disconnect overload currents. As the current increases the temperature rises causing the bi-metal to bend and operate the device. The rate at which the overcurrent current increases will directly affect the time the device operates.

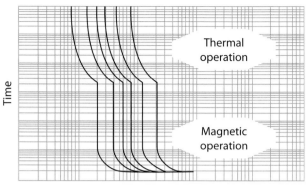

Figure 2.9 *Typical characteristics for miniature circuit breakers to BS EN 60898*

The magnetic component (item 7 in Figure 2.8), is responsible for dealing with high fault current and short circuits. As this operates like a solenoid, the switching action is immediate and there is no gradual change with current increase. When the magnetic device operates, the device disconnects within a nominal 0.1 second and increasing the current will not affect this part of the operation, and so the time current curve is represented as a vertical line.

If we look at the curves for the types B, C and D shown in Figure 2.10, we see that the length of the curve increases and the slope decreases as we go from Type B to C to D. This means that the amount of overload current which can flow is increased and the time taken to disconnect in the event of an overload or short circuit is increased. These characteristics are useful as there are situations where a device that is less sensitive to overload is required.

For example:

1 Circuits which include a significant inductive load, such as a discharge lighting circuit, will introduce an overcurrent, higher than the I_b for the circuit, at the moment they are

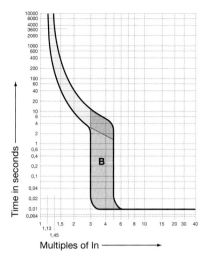

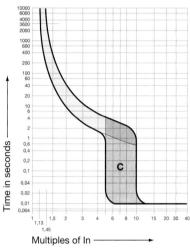

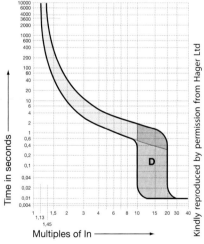

Kindly reproduced by permission from Hager Ltd

Figure 2.10 *Comparison of breaker characteristics*

switched on. As the back EMF is built up, the circuit current falls back to the normal I_b value for the circuit.

2 Circuits with high inductive loads, such as ac motors, may experience a very high starting current, up to $10 \times I_b$, until rotation is achieved when the circuit current will fall back to I_b.

Note

There is more information on the effects of inductive loads and ac motors in the *Principles of Design, Installation and Maintenance* study guide in this Electrical Installation series.

If we were to use a general purpose BS EN 60898 type B circuit breaker for either of these circuits the most likely result is that the circuit breaker will see this larger current as on overcurrent and will operate when the circuit is switched on. So for example 1 we would use a type C circuit breaker and for example 2 we would use a type D circuit breaker.

In general terms the type C breaker will require twice the current of a type B circuit breaker to operate within the same time. A type D circuit breaker will take four times the current of a type B (twice that of a type C) to operate within the same time.

Before circuit breakers were Types A. B C and D they were known as Types 1, 2, 3 and 4. These had similar characteristic differences with the higher the number the more current required to achieve similar disconnection times to lower numbered types.

Effect on fault protection

These characteristics require careful consideration if we are to use the device to provide fault protection. Effectively, the maximum acceptable earth fault loop impedance for the type C device will be half that of the type B. The type D device will be a quarter of the value for a type B device and half that for a type C.

Short circuit

Having considered the operational characteristics we need to consider the implications of short circuit currents.

Example:

A system comprises a supply with a Line to Neutral impedance of 0.05Ω and a circuit with a Line to Neutral impedance of 0.3Ω. If the supply voltage is 230V then at the incoming terminals of the supply we have a fault current of:

$$I = \frac{V}{R} = \frac{230}{0.05} = 4600A \text{ or } 4.6kA$$

At the furthest point on the circuit we will have a prospective fault current of:

$$I = \frac{V}{R} = \frac{230}{0.35} = 657A \text{ or } 0.657kA$$

Where within the system the short circuit occurs will determine the fault current that flows, but we can see that this current may be very high. Any protective device must be able to safely disconnect the fault current that may occur at the point it is located within the system. Our protective device at the origin would need to be able to safely disconnect a current of 4.6kA.

Fault current capacities

Typical prospective fault current ratings are shown in Table 2.2. Similar information is contained in IET Guidance Note 3 and the IET On-Site Guide. More specific information may be obtained from the manufacturer of the particular device to be used.

Remember

When replacing a fuse or circuit breaker it is essential to use a device with the same characteristics which includes type, I_n rating, PFC (protective fault current) rating.

Task

Before continuing with this chapter refer to BS 7671 and complete the table below:

Device BS	Type	I_n	Maximum Z_s	I_a	Disconnection time
BS 88	2	63A			0.4s
BS 88	3	32A	0.96Ω		
BS 3036			1.12Ω	205A	5.0s
BS EN 60898	B	16A			5.0s
BS EN 61009	D	16A			0.4s

Table 2.2 *Typical protective device short circuit ratings*

Device standard	Device type	Rated short-circuit capacity (kA)
BS 88-2		50 at 415V
BS 88-3	type 1 type 2	16 9
Circuit-breakers to BS EN 60898 and RCBOs to BS EN 61009		Icn 1.5 3.0 6.0 10 15 20 25
Earlier standards (withdrawn or superseded)		
Semi-enclosed fuse to BS 3036	S1A S2A S4A	1 2 4
Cartridge fuse to BS 1361	type 1 type 2	16.5 33.0
BS 88-6		16.5 at 240V 80 at 415V
Circuit-breakers to BS 3871 (replaced by BS EN 60898)	M1 M1.5 M3 M4.5 M6 M9	1.0 1.5 3.0 4.5 6.0 9.0

Part 4 Discrimination

Protective devices are installed in the installation to protect the cables and it is not practical to protect a complete installation with a single protective device. To do so means that the device would need to be rated for the full load of the installation and therefore so would all the cables. In practice we use a distribution arrangement to allow suitable sized cables to be used which are more appropriate for the load. This involves using a number of protective devices which are often connected in series.

A typical distribution arrangement for an installation is shown in Figure 2.11 where there are a number of fuses between the supply intake position and the final load of a table lamp connected to the socket outlet circuit.

The objective of discrimination is to make sure that an overcurrent occurring at any point on the system causes the minimum disruption of supply. To do this we must ensure that the fuse on the supply side closest to the cause of

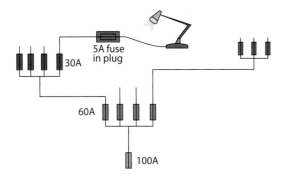

Figure 2.11 *Typical distribution arrangement*

the 45A circuit, the fuse supplying the distribution board may operate and all three final circuits would then be disconnected from the supply.

In Figure 2.13 the 45A fuse supplying the board has been uprated to 60A. Now should the same fault occur on the 45A circuit the circuit fuse will operate, leaving the other two circuits unaffected.

overcurrent operates first and leaves the other devices intact, thus minimizing the number of circuits or appliances affected. So should a fault occur on our table lamp only the lamp should be disconnected from the supply by the plug fuse, leaving everything else functioning normally.

Let us look at a couple of examples of discrimination in practice.

In Figure 2.12, the design for this part of a system has a 45A fuse supplying a distribution board, which supplies three circuits, one of 45A, one of 15A and one of 5A. Should a fault occur on

Remember

The cables must now be selected based upon the sizes of protective devices required to provide discrimination.

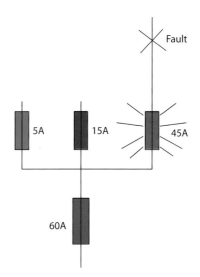

Figure 2.13 *Discrimination is achieved*

In most instances the actual load is less than the rating of the protective device. For example, a domestic lighting circuit is protected by a 6A BSEN 60898 type B circuit breaker. The lighting circuit comprises six lights, for which we must allow a load of 100 Watts per lighting outlet. This gives a total of 600W requiring a full load current of:

$$I = \frac{P}{V} = \frac{600}{230} = 2.6\,A$$

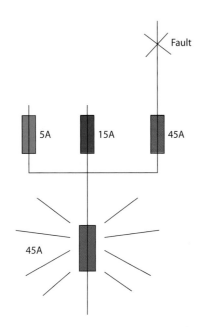

Figure 2.12 *Discrimination is not achieved*

So it is possible that the rating of a protective device is not truly representative of the actual load. This may result in the scenario shown in Figure 2.13 where the 60A fuse is supplying protective devices totalling 65A.

In practice, the loading of all circuits should be considered before the installation begins so that the correct rating and type of protective devices can be installed. To change the protective device for one of another type or rating after completion may require extensive alterations.

In many installations the fuse at the origin is carrying the load current which is shared by a number of protective devices downstream. Effectively this device may be carrying close to its rated current (I_n) so any overcurrent is likely to overload this device first and thereby cause unwanted interruption to the whole installation. Diversity has to be carefully considered during the design stage to minimize the likelihood of this happening.

Remember

The protection device closest to the fault on the supply side is the one that should operate.

Try this

A 1kW electric fire is plugged into a 13A socket outlet. The socket is protected by a 32A circuit breaker in a consumer unit. The main fuse protecting the supply cable (meter tails) and the consumer unit is 100A BS88-2.

Draw a line diagram showing all the fuses and circuit breakers and state which device will operate if the 13A socket outlet develops a short circuit.

Part 5 Protective devices

Fuses

The fuse was once the most common type of overcurrent protection device in use. These devices have been around for more than 120 years providing protection against all types of overcurrents.

In their simplest form fuses consist of a small diameter wire installed in the circuit. If an excessive amount of current begins to flow in the circuit this piece of wire gets hot. As the current flow increases it gets hotter and hotter until it finally melts and opens the circuit, and we say the fuse has 'blown'.

However, not all fuses are made in the same way so let's look at the various types of fuses in use.

Semi-enclosed fuse (BS 3036)

This is the good old 'rewireable' fuse and there are thousands of these installed throughout the world.

It is known as a semi-enclosed fuse because the fuse element is only partially enclosed between the carrier and the base. When the carrier is removed, the fuse wire may be easily seen, and the wire element can be replaced when necessary.

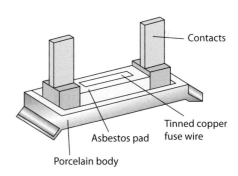

Figure 2.15 *Semi-enclosed fuse BS 3036*

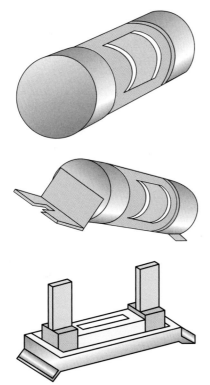

Figure 2.14 *Common types of fuse*

The main **advantages** of this type are that:

● they are relatively cheap
● they are easily repaired
● they are fairly reliable
● it is easy to store spare wire
● it is easy to see when a fuse has blown.

These are just some of the reasons why this type of fuse was once the most widely used overcurrent protection device. However, there are some disadvantages, the effects of which have been to significantly reduce the use of this fuse in favour of other types of device.

The main **disadvantages** are that:

● they are easily abused, the wrong size of fuse wire being fitted accidentally or intentionally
● they require a high current to ensure their operation within the required times (high fusing factor), around 2.5 I_n, and as a result the cables they protect must have a larger current carrying capacity
● the precise conditions for operation cannot be easily predicted
● they do not cope well with high short circuit currents
● the wire can deteriorate over a period of time.

Cartridge fuse BS 88-3 (Replacing BS 1361)

This fuse uses the same principle of a single fuse wire but this time the wire is enclosed in a ceramic or glass body.

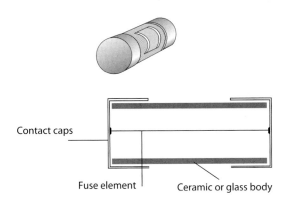

Figure 2.16 *Cartridge fuse BS 88-3 (1361)*

Because it is enclosed the behaviour of the fuse element under overcurrent conditions can be more accurately predicted.

Main **advantages** of this type are that:

● they have a lower fusing factor, around 1.5 times I_n
● they are less prone to abuse
● being totally enclosed the element does not 'scatter' when it fuses
● they are fairly cheap
● they are easy to replace
● they cope better with short circuit currents.

Main **disadvantages** are that:

● they are more expensive than BS 3036
● it is not easy to see if the fuse has blown
● stocks of spare cartridges need to be kept.

This type is a reasonably cheap, more predictable, alternative to the BS 3036 rewireable fuse.

When the filament vaporizes, the scattering metal particles are contained within the ceramic body and so present far less of a fire risk than the BS 3036 type.

BS 88-2 High breaking capacity (HBC) fuse

This fuse is the top of the range with a more sophisticated construction, which makes its operation far more predictable.

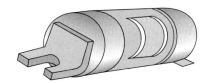

Figure 2.17 *BS 88-2 fuse*

Try this

Using a manufacturer's catalogue, list the ratings of the BS 88-3 fuses available.

A number of silver strips are used to make up the fuse element and these are shaped similarly to those shown in Figure 2.18. This construction means each individual strip can have a low current carrying capacity. This in turn gives the fuse a far more accurate operation. Once overcurrent occurs, the first element to 'blow' increases the current flow through the others and so they operate rapidly in an avalanche effect.

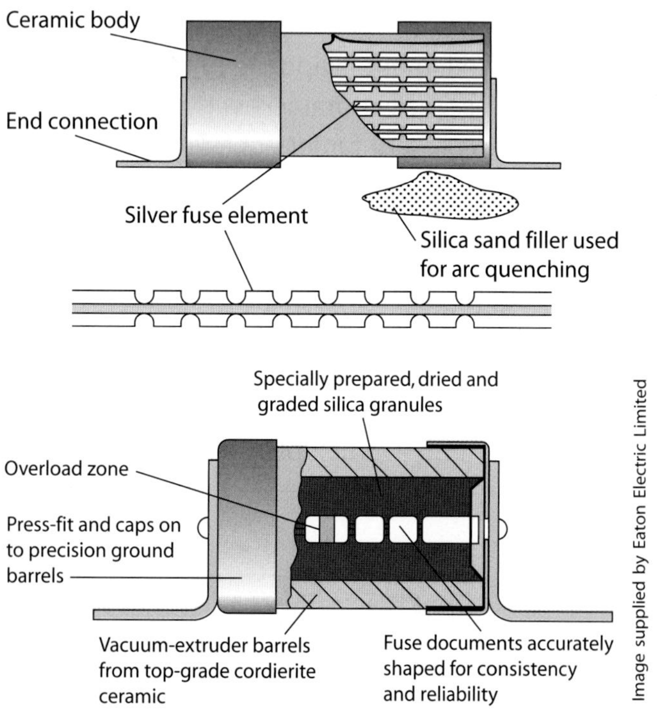

The air space within the fuse body is filled with silica sand. This silica sand filler falls into the gap created by the melting elements and extinguishes the arc that is produced. This type of fuse can break short circuit currents, in the order of 80,000A (80kA).

The main **advantages** of this type of fuse are that they:

- have a low fusing factor, often less than 1.3
- have an ability to break high currents
- are reliable
- are accurate.

Ceramic body

End connection

Silver fuse element

Silica sand filler used for arc quenching

Specially prepared, dried and graded silica granules

Overload zone

Press-fit and caps on to precision ground barrels

Vacuum-extruder barrels from top-grade cordierite ceramic

Fuse documents accurately shaped for consistency and reliability

Image supplied by Eaton Electric Limited

Figure 2.18 *Typical BS 88-2 fuse construction*

The main **disadvantages** of the BS 88-2 are that:

● they are expensive
● stocks of these as spares are costly and take up space
● care must be taken to replace them with not only the same rating of fuse but with one having the same characteristics.

Circuit breakers

Instead of using fuses for protection against overcurrent we can use devices known as circuit breakers. These come in two main categories for internal use:

● circuit breakers (CBs)
● moulded case circuit breakers (MCCBs).

As we established earlier in this chapter, these devices employ a set of contacts which are automatically opened when an overcurrent occurs. This is achieved by using thermal trips for overload and magnetic trips for short circuit.

Circuit breakers BSEN 60898 (BS 3871)

These are used in many domestic and commercial installations.

They have the **advantages** of:

● only needing to be reset after operation so no stock of replacements is required
● the setting cannot usually be adjusted
● being able to discriminate between harmless transient overloads and yet can still cater for short circuit faults
● being easy to identify the breaker that has tripped.

Figure 2.19 *Typical circuit breakers*

The main **disadvantages** of these are that they:

● are expensive
● are mechanical; physically opening the switch to break the current flow
● cannot be used if the short circuit current exceeds their short circuit rating.

Using a mechanical switch to open circuits also creates an arc. For smaller CBs the gap created between the contacts is sufficient to ensure that any arc is extinguished. When operating at higher current levels, and where high short circuit currents may be encountered, the circuit breaker must include some method of extinguishing the arc created. Arc splitters are fitted for this purpose.

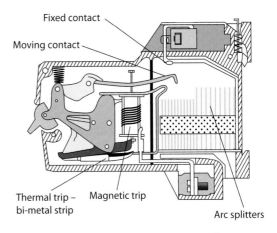

Figure 2.20 *Section across a typical circuit breaker*

Moulded case circuit breakers

Having considered the construction of the circuit breaker, the MCCB is really a more sophisticated version. The ability to break larger fault currents with this device is as a result of a more refined contact and arc control system. We can see from Figure 2.21 that one method of achieving this involves an additional set of contacts, the arcing contacts, with arc runners and an arc chute with splitter plates.

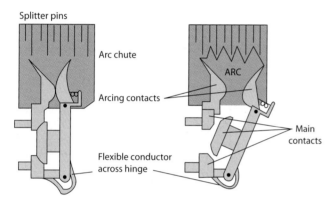

Figure 2.21 *Moulded case circuit breaker*

When the main contacts separate, the arcing contacts remain together and the arc is only initiated when the 'arcing pair' separate. The vaporization and heat distortion to the contacts are confined to the arcing pair. As these do not need to carry the load current during normal operation they can be made of a material such as carbon. The arc is drawn out along the route of the arc chute and the splitter plates extend the arc to create a longer run within a more confined physical space.

Alternative manufacturers' designs deal with arc control in a number of different ways but the common feature is the design of the arc chute. It is the function of the chute to increase the length of the arc as rapidly as possible over the greatest possible distance. The more able we are to do this and control the energy released, the higher the fault current we can disconnect.

The balance between the thermal and magnetic operators does not really affect the fault current control as with high currents the magnetic part of the device should operate far quicker than the thermal trip, which is better placed to deal with lower overload currents. Most MCCBs have an adjustment incorporated to enable us to control the sensitivity of the device to suit various loads, hence a greater versatility from a single device.

Having considered the most common varieties of protective device, there are some circuit breakers, primarily used on the supply network and in industrial installations, which use particular methods of arc control. We shall consider the most common methods of arc control for use in particular applications before we continue.

Oil filled

In this instance the principle of arc control incorporates immersion of the contacts in oil. The contacts are usually contained in an explosion pot constructed to aid the extinguishing of the arc. When the contacts are opened, an arc is drawn through the oil, an insulator, and gases are produced, with a little oil being carbonized in this process.

The pressure caused by the gas is used to force the oil around within the explosion pot, and across the arc, helping to extinguish it, the oil prevents

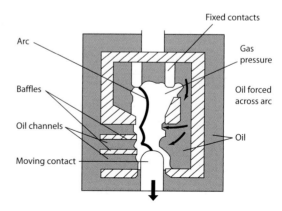

Figure 2.22 *Circuit breaker explosion pot action*

the arc and its by-products from entering the atmosphere. In some breakers the oil is pumped across the contacts to extinguish the arc rather than rely on the pressure of the gas produced.

> **Remember**
> The oil used in transformers and circuit breakers, although contained in flameproof enclosures, is a fire and health hazard. Extreme care should be taken with the handling of oil during maintenance.

Air blast

Figure 2.23 shows the much simplified layout of an air-blast circuit breaker. As the contacts open a blast of compressed air, at around 20 bar, is forced across the arc rapidly extending its length and this quickly extinguishes it. The precise design of these breakers does vary, dependent upon the manufacturer and operational requirements. Some, for example, use a spring mechanism to open the contacts whilst others use the compressed air to open the contacts and extinguish the arc.

Obviously there is considerably more equipment required to operate this type of breaker. Air reservoirs, compressors, operating control gear and the like makes this type more complex and so there is a higher initial cost. On the plus side,

however, the arcing time is shorter, maintenance is cleaner and easier and the fire risk is negligible.

Gas

The operation of this circuit breaker is very similar to that of the air-blast circuit breaker except that a gas, such as carbon hexafluoride, is used. This is a better insulator than air or oil, is non-toxic and non-flammable, inert and stable. The gas, at around 4 bar, surrounds the contacts, as they open a blast of gas at around 16 bar is forced across the arc.

Certain precautions are necessary with this type of breaker such as the installation of heaters in certain locations to prevent the gas from liquefying at low temperatures, say 9 or 10 °C. As the gas is expensive, it is usual to pump it into a storage tank during maintenance and for checks to be made regularly to detect leakage.

Vacuum

The vacuum circuit breaker is relatively maintenance free as the contacts are contained within a sealed vacuum container with the moving contact connected to the outside through a bellows arrangement as shown in Figure 2.24. The contact surfaces are in the form of flat discs and, being contained in a vacuum, there is no other medium to cause ionization.

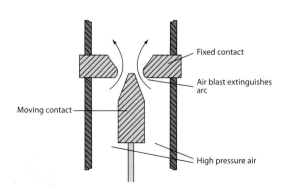

Figure 2.23 *Air-blast circuit breaker*

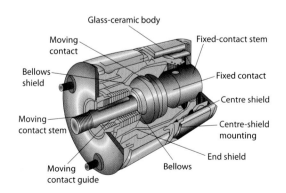

Figure 2.24 *Vacuum circuit breaker*

Try this

Identify the type of protective device most appropriate for the following locations/installations:

a   a domestic consumer unit in a new dwelling

_____

_____

b   a high current using machine circuit in an industrial location

_____

_____

c   a main circuit breaker for a large car manufacturing plant

_____

_____

The result is that the arc is extinguished the first time the current passes through zero on the waveform, with minimum damage to the contact faces.

Residual current devices (RCDs)

These devices detect earth fault currents by measuring current flowing into and current flowing out of an installation or circuit and comparing the two. If there is a difference between the two currents the 'missing current' must have returned by an alternative route, generally a current flow to earth.

In an RCD there are two main windings wound on an iron core and these carry the line and neutral currents. Each coil will produce a magnetic field which is directly proportional to the current that flows through it. In normal conditions these two currents will be of the same value and will consequently produce the same amount of magnetic flux.

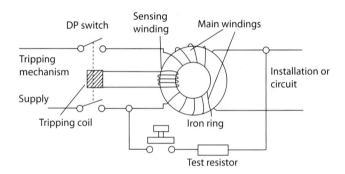

Figure 2.25 *Typical RCD circuit*

As the two currents flow in opposite directions, the magnetic fluxes in the ring will cancel each other out and so the magnetic field in the iron ring is zero.

If some current flows to earth then the line current will be larger than the neutral current.

This means that the magnetic fluxes will no longer cancel out and a magnetic flux will circulate in the iron ring.

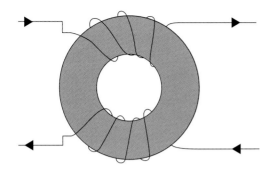

Figure 2.26 *Iron core with windings*

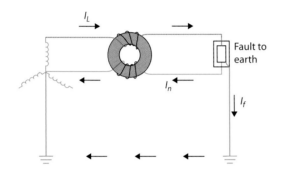

Figure 2.27 *Leakage current results in* $I_L = I_n + I_f$

This residual flux is used to induce a small current into a sensing coil, and when this reaches a pre-set level the current flowing in this coil is sufficient to operate a small solenoid, which in turn releases the powerful spring and a tripping mechanism opens the main contacts isolating the supply. (See Figure 2.25).

As we learnt earlier RCDs may be used to provide protection:

- where a suitably low earth fault loop impedance cannot be achieved
- in areas of increased shock risk.

It may be necessary to have more than one RCD connected in series, for example on a TT system. We may require an RCD at the origin of the installation because the earth fault loop impedance is too high. However, where there are socket outlets rated at ≤ 20A additional protection will also be required. In such cases we may

have a 100mA at the origin and a 30mA RCD for the socket outlet circuit connected in series. In this case the 100mA RCD will need to be of the Selective or Time Delay type in order to prevent nuisance tripping. This is much the same as the requirement for discrimination with our overcurrent devices.

Residual current breaker with overcurrent (RCBO)

We also need to consider the use of RCBOs which combine the overcurrent protection features of a circuit breaker with the fault current protection of an RCD. This combination allows a single unit to provide both functions and therefore each circuit is individually protected against fault currents minimizing inconvenience in the event of a fault. Many RCBOs have a functional earth connection, the colour for this conductor is cream and can be seen connected to the earth bar in Figure 2.28.

MK Electric

Figure 2.28 *Consumer unit fitted with circuit breakers and RCBOs*

As RCDs and RCBOs monitor the balance of current between the line conductors nuisance tripping may occur due to the normal operation of the circuits. For example, inductive loads may cause an imbalance during switching on and off and heating elements often produce leakage currents when they are switched on.

Where a number of circuits are protected by a single RCD the device is subject to the combined current imbalance for all the circuits and when it operates all the circuits will be disconnected. The use of an RCBO will help to minimize nuisance tripping as the device is only subject to the current imbalance for the single circuit it supplies. Similarly, when it operates only that particular circuit is disconnected from the supply. However, there is an additional cost implication for the RCBO.

Task

a   Use BS 7671 to determine three different locations where an RCD is to be used for additional protection.

b   Identify the maximum rating of the RCD in each location identified in a. above.

Part 6 Earthing and fault protection

Earth fault loop impedance

In Chapter 1 of this study guide we considered the earth fault paths for the various systems available on the public distribution network. We need to consider the requirements and implications of the TT and PME earthing systems on our electrical installations in a little more detail here.

TT systems

As the earth fault return path for the TT system relies on the general mass of earth for the return path, the DNO is unable to give a figure for the external loop path of this system. In almost all cases the earth return path external to the installation on the TT system is quite a high resistance and as a result we need to provide fault protection by use of an RCD.

The use of a single 30mA RCD is not appropriate to protect the whole installation for the nuisance tripping reasons discussed earlier in this chapter. However split load distribution boards are available which incorporate a number of 30mA RCDs and the installation is divided across these to minimize any nuisance tripping.

We need to determine the external earth fault path for the TT installation and confirm that it is suitable to allow the RCD to disconnect within the required time. The basis for this is derived from the formula:

$$50V = R_A \times I_{\Delta n} \text{ where}$$

- 50V is the maximum touch voltage
- $I_{\Delta n}$ is the operating current of the RCD, and
- R_A is the resistance of the earth electrode.

BS 7671 states that as the installation is part of a TT system and protected by an RCD we can use the Z_e for the installation as the R_A value.

If we need to know the maximum R_A for an earth electrode we need to rearrange the formula to give

$$R_A. \text{ So } \frac{50V}{I_{\Delta n}} = R_A$$

and for the standard ratings of RCD we can determine the maximum R_A.

For a 30 mA RCD the maximum R_A is $\dfrac{50}{0.03} = 1667\,\Omega$

For a 100 mA RCD the maximum R_A is $\dfrac{50}{0.1} = 500\,\Omega$

For a 300 mA RCD the maximum R_A is $\dfrac{50}{0.3} = 167\,\Omega$

For a 500 mA RCD the maximum R_A is $\dfrac{50}{0.5} = 100\,\Omega$

However, BS 7671 states that any value above 200Ω is likely to be unstable and so despite the high values for the 30mA and 100mA RCDs the actual value should not exceed 200Ω.

Note

This requirement is considered again in more detail in the study guide *Inspection, Testing and Commissioning* of this Electrical Installation series.

Protective multiple earthing (PME)

Protective multiple earthing (PME) is a very common system used by the DNO and is essentially a TN-C-S system with additional earth electrodes installed on the DNO's PEN conductor as shown in Figure 2.29. This particular earthing system is outlined in detail in the Electricity Safety, Quality and Continuity Regulations (ESQCR).

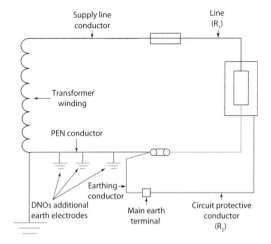

Figure 2.29 *PME earthing system*

The purpose of the additional earth electrodes is to maintain the PEN conductor at or about earth potential and minimize danger should the neutral be lost (disconnected or cut through). One of the significant statements in the ESQCR is that the protective conductors of a PME system are not to be connected to the metalwork of a caravan or boat (or similar structure).

So a caravan park or marina may use a PME system for the office, facilities blocks (toilets, showers, etc.) but not for the sockets supplying the caravans or boats. In practice the supplies to these sockets would be made to a separate TT system on the site.

Inspection of the intake position of the installation will not enable the electrician to determine whether the system is a TN-C-S or PME as the additional electrodes cannot be seen. For this reason the DNO attaches a label at the origin where the supply is PME.

Figure 2.30 *Typical PME label*

Task

Using the drawings below complete and label the earth fault path for each of the systems.

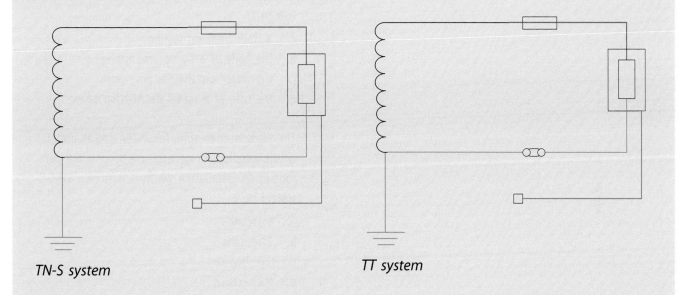

TN-S system

TT system

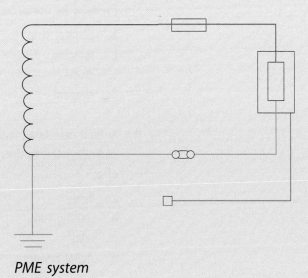

PME system

Congratulations, you have now completed Chapter 2 of this study guide. Complete the self assessment questions before progressing to Chapter 3.

SELF ASSESSMENT

Circle the correct answers.

1   Which of the following is an extraneous conductive part?

   a.   a steel trunking system
   b.   the body of a fluorescent fitting
   c.   the water installation pipe work
   d.   the case of a metal distribution board

2   The disconnection time for a 26A socket outlet circuit installed for general use by ordinary persons in an installation which is part of a TN-C-S system is:

   a.   5 seconds
   b.   2 seconds
   c.   0.4 seconds
   d.   0.2 seconds

3   A circuit breaker provides protection against overload by use of a:

   a.   bimetal strip
   b.   solenoid
   c.   diode
   d.   element

4   An RCD detects an imbalance in the circuit current and relays this to the operating solenoid by means of a:

   a.   diode
   b.   sensing coil
   c.   relay
   d.   signal resistor

5   A PME system is distinguished from a TN-C-S system because the DNO installs:

   a.   BS 88-3 fuse
   b.   leakage sensor
   c.   overhead conductors
   d.   additional earth electrodes

Progress check

1. **A three-phase, four wire system has a line to neutral voltage of 250V. The voltage between line conductors is:**

   ☐ a. 750V

   ☐ b. 433V

   ☐ c. 144V

   ☐ d. 83V

2. **The nominal supply voltages U/U_0 for a three-phase system in the UK is:**

   ☐ a. 400/230V

   ☐ b. 400/140V

   ☐ c. 415/230V

   ☐ d. 415/240V

3. **The neutral conductor in a balanced three-phase circuit carries:**

   ☐ a. the load current

   ☐ b. the resultant current

   ☐ c. half the load current

   ☐ d. no current at all

4. **The line current of a three-phase load is 53A. The current in the phase winding is:**

   ☐ a. 92A

   ☐ b. 159A

   ☐ c. 31A

   ☐ d. 17.6A

5. **The single-phase supplies to consumers' installations are connected on different phases of the supply to:**

   ☐ a. minimize the inconvenience in the event of a failure of supply

   ☐ b. balance the load on the DNO's equipment

   ☐ c. reduce the DNO's installation costs

   ☐ d. help the jointing process

6. **The maximum distance between the local point of isolation and a domestic cooker is:**

   ☐ a. 5m

   ☐ b. 4m

   ☐ c. 3m

   ☐ d. 2m

7. **The I_n rating of a BS 88-3 fuse indicates the current that the fuse can:**

   ☐ a. safely disconnect under earth fault conditions

   ☐ b. safely disconnect under short circuit conditions

   ☐ c. carry for a short period until the load is reduced

   ☐ d. carry for an indefinite period without deterioration

8. **An increase in load on a healthy electrical circuit may result in:**

☐ a. overload

☐ b. short circuit

☐ c. earth leakage currents

☐ d. no change in circuit conditions

9. **To provide protection against electric shock we use a system of earthing. It is important the earth return path has a:**

☐ a. low resistance

☐ b. high resistance

☐ c. high impedance

☐ d. low impedance

10. **The earthing for a domestic electrical installation has become disconnected. Which of the following statements is not correct?**

☐ a. the supply to the installation will fail

☐ b. the installation will function normally

☐ c. there is a risk of electric shock to the user

☐ d. the fuses will provide earth fault protection

11. **The provision of earthing in an electrical installation maintains an equal potential to all:**

☐ a. exposed conductive parts

☐ b. extraneous conductive parts

☐ c. metalwork in the building

☐ d. structural metalwork

12. **An equal potential on all extraneous conductive parts is achieved by:**

☐ a. main protective bonding conductors

☐ b. supplementary bonding conductors

☐ c. circuit protective conductors

☐ d. cross bonding

13. **The label fixed to a bonding connection should read:**

☐ a. safety earth connection – do not remove

☐ b. safety electrical connection – do not remove

☐ c. electrical earthing connection – do not remove

☐ d. earthing connection for safety – do not remove

14. **The current required to cause a protective device to operate within the required time (I_a) is 350A and the nominal voltage of the circuit (U_0) is 230 volts. The maximum acceptable earth fault loop impedance is:**

☐ a. 0.66Ω

☐ b. 0.86Ω

☐ c. 1.20Ω

☐ d. 1.52Ω

15. The maximum disconnection time for a final circuit which is part of a TT system and is protected by a 16A protective device is:

☐ a. 5s

☐ b. 2s

☐ c. 0.4s

☐ d. 0.2s

16. The DNO quoted maximum external earth fault loop impedance (Z_e) for a TN-S system is:

☐ a. 21Ω

☐ b. 5.5Ω

☐ c. 0.80Ω

☐ d. 0.35Ω

17. The component within a circuit breaker which provides protection against high fault current is a:

☐ a. bimetal strip

☐ b. solenoid

☐ c. diode

☐ d. element

18. To help extinguish the arc produced when operating, the fuse element in a BS88-2 fuse is surrounded by:

☐ a. air

☐ b. a vacuum

☐ c. silica sand

☐ d. glass

19. A residual current device (RCD) is used to provide protection against:

☐ a. overload current

☐ b. short circuit current

☐ c. earth fault current

☐ d. induced current

20. The maximum earth fault loop impedance for a 100mA RCD to operate within the required time is:

☐ a. 100Ω

☐ b. 167Ω

☐ c. 500Ω

☐ d. 1667Ω

3

Cable and circuit protective device selection

RECAP

Before you start work on this chapter, complete the exercise below to ensure that you remember what you learned earlier.

- Exposed conductive parts are part of the _____ installation which are conductive and can be _____.

- A circuit _____ conductor shall be run to and _____ at each _____ in the wiring and at _____ accessory.

- Main protective _____ conductors are used to connect the _____ conductive parts to the main _____ terminal.

- _____ bonding is primarily used in areas of increased _____ risk.

- The maximum declared values of _____ given by the DNO for their systems are TN-S = _____ Ω TN-C-S = _____ Ω.

- An overload occurs in a _____ circuit and current often _____ up over _____.

- A _____ circuit occurs _____ and causes a _____ current to flow.

- The objective of discrimination is to make sure that an _____ occurring at any point on the _____ causes the _____ disruption of supply.

- A circuit breaker provides protection against _____ by using _____ trips and uses _____ trips for _____ circuit.

- A residual current device detects _____ fault currents by measuring current flowing _____ and current flowing _____ an installation or circuit and _____ the two.

- The DNO is unable to give a figure for the external earth _____ loop _____ path TT system as the return _____ relies on the _____.

LEARNING OBJECTIVES

This chapter considers the selection of cables and protective devices for electrical installations and the selection of containment systems. You will need to refer to BS 7671 and IET Guidance Note 1, when you are working through this chapter. You may also find the IET On-Site Guide helpful.

On completion of this chapter you should be able to:

- Explain how external influences can affect your choice of wiring systems and enclosures.

- State the current ratings for different circuit protection devices.

- State the procedure for selecting appropriate overcurrent protection devices.

- Select suitable size cables, conduit and trunking as appropriate.

- State what is meant by diversity factors and explain how a circuit's maximum demand is established after diversity factors are applied.

Part 1 External influences

Before choosing a wiring system for a particular installation the person responsible for the design should be fully aware of any external influences which are likely to be encountered during the foreseeable lifetime of the installation.

Let's start by considering some of the environmental conditions which may be encountered by an electrical installation.

Environmental conditions

Temperature

High or low temperatures will have an effect on most materials used in cable production. The temperature will also have an effect on enclosures and equipment and therefore we must select these accordingly.

For example, although PVC may not become brittle until around −5°C it can be damaged when installed at temperatures around 0°C. Carrying out the installation of PVC materials at these temperatures may damage cables and PVC conduit. Similarly, the upper ambient temperature for PVC is around 60°C and so this material should not be used where the ambient temperature may exceed this.

Where conditions outside the ambient temperature range for materials exist they will be more prone to damage; PVC in a low temperature may be split and cracked by an impact which would not affect it at a higher temperature. The materials selected should always be suitable for the range of ambient temperatures in which they will operate.

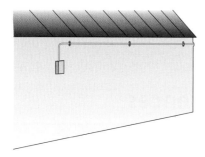

Figure 3.1 *PVC cable heated by the sun can become hot and the insulation degrade*

Figure 3.2 *Cold store room*

Humidity

Having given consideration to the effects of the temperature that may exist we must also make allowance for humidity, i.e. the moisture content of the air. This relates to the water content of the atmosphere compared with the total mass of the air. It is not the same as water droplets or rain.

One effect of humidity may be demonstrated by considering the effect of condensation forming on a person's glasses when coming indoors from the cold. Condensation (moisture) forms rapidly on the lenses of the glasses but there is no obvious evidence of moisture in the air. This effect occurs due to the difference in temperature and the presence of the moisture within the air.

In areas where there is a very high level of humidity there is often a considerable build up of condensation with water pooling and dripping onto equipment.

Where low humidity exists there is a greater risk of a build-up of static electricity which may affect electronic equipment when the static discharges.

These conditions can have a considerable impact on electrical and electronic equipment and consideration must be given when selecting materials and equipment.

Figure 3.3 *Electrical installations in greenhouses have to be suitable for the humid environment*

Water

By this we mean the likelihood of water being present in the area. In general this can be viewed in terms of water droplets and the direction in which these droplets are travelling. In some locations there may be high levels of water present, such as in a shower room, and equipment may be subject to splashing, sprays or jets of water.

Materials used in these conditions must be suitable for their environment and care must be taken in the selection process. Cables and enclosures subject to these conditions must be confirmed as maintaining their physical properties, so will not rust for example, and prevent penetration by liquids.

Figure 3.4 *Car washes and street lighting have to be wired in cables suitable for wet conditions*

Also the construction process should not reduce the level of protection afforded by the equipment. Holes, cable access points, spare ways in distribution boards and the like should be reinstated to maintain the level of protection required.

Foreign bodies

We can look at this in two stages: first, as the amount of dust and debris that will be present in the air. A general office environment is likely to produce very little dust whereas a flour mill or wood machining workshop may produce high levels of dust. Second, and this applies generally to enclosures, the likelihood of objects such as tools, fingers or materials being inserted whilst the equipment is live.

Figure 3.5 *Wood machining workshop*

The selection of appropriate materials to prevent impregnation by dust, debris and objects must be used and the construction process should not reduce the level of protection afforded by the equipment. Holes, cable access points, spare ways in distribution boards and the like should be reinstated to maintain the level of protection required.

IP code

At this point it is worth considering the use of the IP code, which is from the International Standard IEC 60529, and classifies the level of protection provided by enclosures. The Ingress Protection code identifies levels of protection against the ingress of solid bodies and liquids.

Example of IP code:

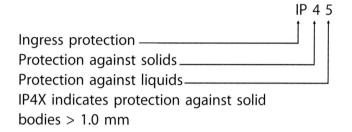

IP 4 5

Ingress protection ⎯⎯⎯⎯⎯⎯⎯⎯⎯⎯⎯
Protection against solids ⎯⎯⎯⎯⎯⎯
Protection against liquids ⎯⎯⎯⎯⎯
IP4X indicates protection against solid bodies > 1.0 mm

IPX5 indicates protection against liquids sprayed on the equipment

The use of X in the code indicates that particular consideration is not necessary for the location. So equipment in a general office would not normally require protection against liquids and therefore the second digit would be replaced with an X.

Table 3.1 shows the basic IP code and we can see that the protection against solid bodies is in the range from 0 to 6 and the protection against liquids is in the range 0 to 8. We can use this information to determine the requirements for the equipment relevant to these conditions.

Additional letters may also be used to identify levels of protection against access to live parts by persons. These are shown in Table 3.2.

Table 3.2 *Additional letters*

Additional letter	Level of protection afforded
A	Back of the hand
B	Finger (12mm)
C	Tool (2.5mm)
D	Wire (1.0mm)

Table 3.1 *Basic IP code*

1st digit	Level of protection	2nd digit	Level of protection
0	Not protected	0	Not protected
1	Protected against solid foreign objects of 50mm diameter and greater	1	Protected against vertically falling water drops
2	Protected against solid foreign objects of 12.5mm diameter and greater	2	Protected against vertically falling water drops when enclosure is tilted up to 15°
3	Protected against solid foreign objects of 2.5mm diameter and greater	3	Protected against water sprayed at an angle up to 60° on either side of the vertical
4	Protected against solid foreign objects of 1.0mm diameter and greater	4	Protected against water splashed against the component from any direction
5	Protected from the amount of dust that would interfere with normal operation	5	Protected against water projected in jets from any direction
6	Dust tight	6	Protected against water projected in powerful jets from any direction and heavy seas
No code		7	Protected against temporary immersion in water
No code		8	Protected against continuous immersion in water, or as specified by the user

BS 7671 refers to these additional letters when referring to protection against human activity as opposed to environmental hazards. The code for these is generally given as IPXXB for example, which is the minimum requirement for all surfaces of equipment except the top surface. The requirement for accessible top surfaces is IPXXD.

These additional letters are related to the protection of persons and should not be confused with the environmental codes for solid bodies, although they are considered as equivalents in BS 7671.

Corrosive or polluting substances

In any area where corrosive or polluting substances are likely to be present we must take particular account of the materials used for the installation and their suitability for such an environment.

Figure 3.7 *The effects of corrosion on metal conduits*

Mechanical impact

There are many situations where cables are installed and are likely to become damaged due to mechanical impact. We must ensure that suitable protection is provided in such instances. The IEC Standard IEC 62262 refers to IK ratings which is an international standard for classifying the degree of protection offered by electrical equipment enclosures. It is used as a method of specifying the ability of an enclosure to protect the contents from external impact. An example of IK codes is given in Table 3.3.

Table 3.3 *IK code*

IK ratings		
IK number	Impact	Equivalent impact
00	No protection	None
01	0.15 joules	200g object dropped from 7.5cm
02	0.2 joules	200g object dropped from 10cm
03	0.35 joules	200g object dropped from 17.5cm
04	0.5 joules	200g object dropped from 25cm
05	0.7 joules	200g object dropped from 35cm
06	1 joules	500g object dropped from 20cm

www.platingsales.com

Figure 3.6 *Electro plating baths can give off corrosive fumes*

(Continued)

Table 3.3 *Continued*

IK number	Impact	Equivalent impact
07	2 joules	500g object dropped from 40cm
08	5 joules	1.7kg object dropped from 29.5cm
09	10 joules	5kg object dropped from 20cm
10	20 joules	5kg object dropped from 40cm

Vibration

Where a wiring system is connected to a machine there is likely to be some vibration and an allowance must be made for this when selecting the method of connection to the fixed wiring system.

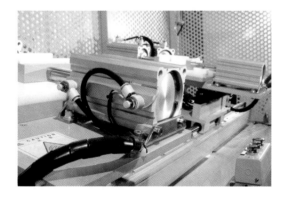

Figure 3.8 *Machines often produce vibration*

Flora or mould growth

This is similar to the consideration that we gave to corrosive substances as many plants and moulds produce corrosive chemicals. Plants may also attract wildlife with the risk of physical damage as well as the increased chemical risk from urine and faeces which are corrosive substances.

Solar radiation

If we intend carrying out an installation where some part is exposed to the effects of sunlight then we must ensure that the system of wiring and the materials used are suitable for such exposure.

The effects are twofold. First, there is the effect of solar gain, whereby the cables absorb heat from the sun. This increase in temperature may cause the cable to operate at a higher temperature and this will degrade the insulation.

Second, there is the effect of ultraviolet radiation which causes the material to degrade over time. Cables and equipment for installation in these conditions generally contain carbon black or other UV stabilizers to minimize the effects of exposure.

Shielding or additional protection within an enclosure is an option but consideration must be given to the effects of temperature where this method is used.

Lightning

If part of the system is located outside of a building then we must consider the possibility of a lightning strike to the system and offer the necessary protection to prevent this from creating a hazard to both the system and the user. The installation of lightning protection is a skilled area which is not covered in this series of study guides.

Electromagnetic effects

This covers a number of areas but they are all concerned with the effects of stray electric currents or electromagnetic radiation including electrostatics.

Risk of fire

This area of consideration includes the requirements covering:

- escape routes
- buildings constructed of mainly combustible material
- locations with a risk of fire due to the nature of stored or processed materials
- locations of commercial, national, industrial or public significance
- fire propagating structures.

There are particular requirements in these locations and situations which require materials and equipment which will:

- not promote or assist combustion
- continue to function should such an event take place.

In addition to these considerations we must also have some regard for the effects of natural phenomena such as wind and ground movement.

We must also bear in mind that in certain cases more than one of these conditions will apply at a single location.

> **Note**
>
> IET Guidance Note 1, Selection & Erection, contains further information on the requirements for the selection of materials.

Classification of external influences

Appendix 5 of BS 7671 contains tables which provide a classification of the various external influences, which are extracted from harmonized document HD60364-5-51.

The classification is given in the form of two letters followed by numbers.

For example:

- first letters: A = Environment, B = Utilization, C = Construction of buildings
- second letter relates to the nature of the external influence (A, B, C, D, etc)
- the number relates to the class within each external influence.

So AE6 refers to: Environment – Foreign bodies – Heavy dust.

These classifications are intended to be used to mark equipment and for that we refer to the IP code.

Try this

A distribution circuit is to be installed to a separate building and the route takes the SWA distribution cable fixed to a brick wall through a farmyard. List the environmental conditions which could apply to the supply cable on this section of the route.

- Exposure to _____

- Exposure to _____

● **Exposure to** _____

● **Exposure to** _____

● **Exposure to** _____

● **Exposure to** _____

Task

Refer to Appendix 5 of BS 7671 and determine the conditions which apply for each of the following classification codes.

a AD3 _____

b BE3 _____

c CA2 _____

Part 2   Selecting overcurrent protective devices

Type and rating of protective devices

Before we can begin to look at the process for selecting protective devices and cables we need to be aware of the types and ratings of the protective devices in common use. Some of these common types and ratings are shown in Table 3.4.

In order to select an overcurrent protective device we first need to determine the load of the circuit or installation it is protecting. So the first task is to determine the load current.

Remember

The rating of a protective device I_n is the current it can carry for an indefinite period without deterioration.

Table 3.4 *Fuse and circuit breaker ratings*

BS type	Type	Ratings (A)
Fuses		
BS88-2		6, 10, 16, 20, 25, 32, 40, 50, 63, 80, 100, 125, 160, 200.
BS88-3		5, 16, 20, 32, 45, 63, 80, 100.
BS3036		5, 15, 20, 30, 45, 60, 100.
BS1362		3, 13.
Circuit breakers		
BS EN 60898 BS EN 61009	B,	3, 6, 10, 16, 20, 25, 32, 40, 50, 63, 80, 100, 125.
BS EN 60898 BS EN 61009	C & D	6, 10, 16, 20, 25, 32, 40, 50, 63, 80, 100, 125.

Working out the load current

This is called the 'circuit design current' and is given the symbol I_b and, for a single load or item of equipment, you may find this information on a maker's plate (Figure 3.9).

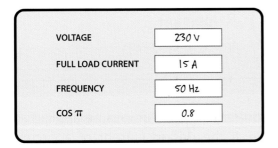

VOLTAGE	230 V
FULL LOAD CURRENT	15 A
FREQUENCY	50 Hz
COS π	0.8

Figure 3.9 *Maker's plate details*

However, for many manufacturers and items of equipment the load current is not given; but the power in watts or kilowatts is provided. From this we need to determine the load current.

For a single load in kilowatts this is not too difficult we simply use the formula:

$$\text{Current} = \frac{\text{Watts}}{\text{Supply voltage} \times \text{power factor}}$$

which is usually written as $I = \dfrac{P}{V \times \cos\theta}$

Power factor is considered in *Principles of Design, Installation and Maintenance* of this series but a brief reminder here will be useful.

Power factor (Symbol: cos θ)

In some ac circuits, particularly where there are inductive loads, the current and voltage are out of step with each other. They do not peak in the waveform at the same time and don't work together as they should. This reduces the amount of power obtained for that current and voltage or, alternatively, more current is drawn from the

supply in order to deliver the power required. Either way it affects the calculated value of load current.

We can consider this using a mechanical example. In Figure 3.10 there are two tractors pulling a log and the maximum power is transmitted through the tow rope when the tractors are pulling in tandem.

Figure 3.10 *Two tractors pulling in tandem*

In Figure 3.11 the two tractors are still exerting a force on the log but there is a reduction in the power transmitted through the tow rope as neither is exerting a straight pull.

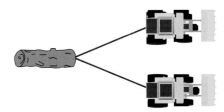

Figure 3.11 *Two tractors not exerting a straight pull*

If we consider this as an electrical example the power factor is an indication of the power loss due to the current and voltage not being in phase (tandem) and more current will be drawn from the supply as a result. If the voltage and current are in phase then the power factor is unity (1).

Example

What is the current drawn by a 6kW load with a power factor of 1.0 connected to a 200V supply?

$$I_b = \frac{6kW \times 1000}{200V \times 1.0} = \frac{6000}{200} = 30A$$

If we now determine the current drawn by a 6kW load with a power factor of 0.6 connected to a 200V supply we get:

$$I_b = \frac{6kW \times 1000}{200V \times 0.6} = \frac{6000}{120} = 50A$$

We can see that to produce the same power the load with the lower power factor draws considerably more current from the supply. In larger installations the DNO penalizes the consumer if their power factor falls to an unacceptable level. This is because their equipment has to supply the current drawn by the load and the poor power factor shows that this is wasted as no more work is achieved.

If a load has no stated power factor this is generally because there is no phase difference between the current and the voltage. This often occurs with loads such as tungsten lighting and heating, and in such cases the power factor (cos θ) is 1. The power factor is always 1 for all direct current (dc) loads.

If we consider the design of a circuit to supply a 3kW heater with a power factor of 1.0 at 230V ac we can determine the load current I_b for the circuit:

$$Ib = \frac{3000}{230} = 13.04A$$

When selecting a protective device for a particular load we must ensure that the rating of the device (I_n) is equal to or greater than the design current (I_b) of the circuit.

The heater is to be supplied from a distribution board which contains BS EN 60898 type B circuit breakers. By reference to the manufacturer's data, BS 7671 or Table 3.4 in this chapter, we can see that the nearest size of circuit breaker is 16A.

Remember

$I_b \leq I_n$ in every case.

This requirement must always be applied so, for example, if the design current of a circuit was 20.5A we could not use a 20A BS EN 60898 circuit breaker for protection and we have to go up to a 25A device.

When calculating the load current for discharge lighting, a fluorescent luminaire for example, we need to make an allowance for this being a discharge luminaire with control gear. This means we cannot use the same process of watts divided by voltage to obtain the current.

We can obtain specific details from the manufacturer of the luminaires, if we know who they are, or we have to use a multiplier to determine the load current. The standard multiplier for this situation is 1.8 so our load current calculation becomes:

$$I_b = \frac{Watts}{Volts} \times 1.8$$

Try this

1 A 230V, 4.6kW load has a power factor of 0.8. What is its load current?

2 A tungsten lighting circuit consists of ten 230V, 100W luminaires, each with a power factor of 1 (unity). What is the circuit design current?

Part 3 Rating factors

Having determined the load current for our circuit we need to select the cable. To do this we must determine whether the live conductors are suitable for the current carrying capacity and voltage drop in the circuit. We also need to consider the thermal constraints placed upon the cable in the event of a fault to earth but we will consider these in the next part of this chapter.

The first thing we need to establish is the minimum current carrying capacity of the live conductors required to supply the load. To do this we need to understand how the capacities are defined.

BS 7671 refers to the current carrying capacity of cables in two terms:

● I_z = the current carrying capacity of a cable in continuous service under particular conditions

● I_t = the tabulated current carrying capacity in Appendix 4 of BS 7671.

There are a number of factors which determine the current carrying capacity of a cable and the values given in BS 7671, Appendix 4, are for cables defined for a single circuit by:

● type of cable
● method of installation
● an ambient temperature of 30°C.

Where other factors affect these criteria then we need to compensate for this during the selection process.

Before we begin, a revision of the intention behind cable selection is appropriate.

The cables used for electrical installations are generally copper or aluminium. When current passes through these materials heat is produced.

In order to not cause damage to the conductors or insulation it is essential that the conductor temperature does not get too high. All conductors used in cables have a maximum operating temperature which should not be exceeded.

For the common insulation materials the maximum conductor operating temperatures are:

- thermoplastic insulation: 70°C
- thermosetting insulation: 90°C.

When selecting cables the current carrying capacities given in Appendix 4 are those which the conductor can carry without exceeding this temperature.

Note

Depending on the load it may take some time for the conductors to reach this normal operating temperature.

The purpose of the cable selection process is to ensure that, under the specific installation conditions for the circuit being considered, this conductor operating temperature is not exceeded.

For the purpose of cable selection, we generally calculate the cable current carrying capacity in order to make the selection from the tables in Appendix 4 of BS 7671. As we have seen these values are based upon a set of criteria which may not apply in every case.

For example, it is quite common for cables to be run grouped with other cables, through areas with an ambient temperature greater or less than 30°C or under other conditions which will affect the current carrying capacity.

In order to determine the cable size required we calculate the minimum I_t value by applying rating factors to compensate for any variations to those conditions used in the Appendix 4 tables. The current carrying capacity can then be used to determined cable size directly from the tables in Appendix 4.

Remember

We calculate the minimum value of current carrying capacity for the cable required by applying rating factors to compensate for any changes in the prescribed conditions for Appendix 4 of BS 7671. By doing this the cable size can then be found directly from the tables in the Appendix 4.

We first need to consider the factors that will affect the current carrying capacity of the cable beginning with ambient temperature.

Ambient temperature

We have already established that the figures given in BS 7671 Appendix 4 are based upon an ambient temperature of 30°C. If the temperature of the surroundings is already high, then the cable will be unable to dissipate as much heat and so cause the cable to exceed its temperature limit.

Of course ambient temperature applies to all locations and cables in air are the most common ones used. However rating factors need to be applied for buried cables, the normal ambient temperature for the ground is taken to be 20°C.

To prevent the cable from overheating in these circumstances we can use a larger cable which will cause less heat to be generated within the

Figure 3.12 *Checking the ambient temperature*

cable. How much larger this cable needs to be will depend on the ambient temperature. Appendix 4 of BS 7671 contains a table of rating factors for different ambient temperatures.

Tables 4B1 to 4B5 provide details of the rating factors to be applied with Table 4B1 giving the rating factors for cables in air.

Table 3.5 shows the rating factors for 70°C thermoplastic insulated cables.

Table 3.5 *Ambient temperature rating factors*

Ambient temperature	70°C thermoplastic insulation
25	1.03
30	1.00
35	0.94
40	0.87
45	0.79

We can see from the figures in Table 3.5 that where the ambient temperature is:

● less than 30°C the rating factor is greater than 1
● 30°C the rating factor is exactly 1
● above 30°C the rating factors become less than one and the higher the temperature the lower the rating factor.

Remember
The ambient temperature to be considered is the normal ambient temperature for the location not the ambient temperature during installation.

The next change to installation conditions to be considered is where cables are not run as an individual circuit. It is common for circuits to share a common route and therefore the cables will be bunched together, which is referred to as grouping.

Grouping

A twin cable, or a pair of single conductors, will generate some heat but this need not be too much of a problem if the heat can escape into the surrounding air.

Where a single enclosure, possibly a conduit or trunking, has several circuits all bunched together, all similarly loaded and all trying to get rid of their own heat then the combined heating effect is going to raise the temperature of the group.

Task
Before you continue with this chapter familiarize yourself with Table 4B1 in BS 7671, Appendix 4.

This means that unless steps have been taken to compensate for this situation all the cables are likely to go above their temperature limit.

The means of compensating for the grouping of cables is by the application of a rating factor for the conditions. The key considerations which affect the factor being used include:

- are the cables all equally loaded?
- how many circuits are there?

The factor is based upon the lowest operating temperature of any cable in the group.

You will notice that we refer to the number of circuits not the number of cables when determining grouping factors. This is because we consider the current per circuit, not per conductor or cable. For example, if we consider a 4 core SWA cable which is supplying a single three-phase load, this is one cable and one circuit. If the same circuit was installed in a trunking containment system there would be four separate conductors but still only one circuit. Similarly, for a ring final circuit installed in a conduit system there would be four live conductors but still only one circuit.

In Appendix 4 of BS 7671, Tables 4C1 to 4C6 are concerned with the grouping of cables under various installation conditions.

Table 3.6 shows some of the rating factors for grouping which relate to some of the most common installation methods. Once again we can see that a single circuit has a rating factor of 1.0 and as the number of circuits in the group increases the rating factor becomes lower. Using reference 1 from the table, once we have 9 cables in a group the rating factor drops to 0.5.

Task

Before you continue with this chapter familiarize yourself with Tables 4C1 to 4C 6 in Appendix 4 of BS 7671.

Table 3.6 *Rating factors for grouping*

Rating factors for groups of circuits or multicore cables								
Reference	Arrangement (touching cables)	Number of circuits						Reference method
		1	2	3	4	5	6	
1	Bunched in air, on a surface embedded or enclosed	1.00	0.80	0.70	0.65	0.60	0.57	A to F
2	Single layer on a wall or floor	1.00	0.85	0.79	0.75	0.73	0.72	C
3	Single layer multicore on a perforated cable tray system	1.00	0.88	0.82	0.77	0.75	0.73	E

Figure 3.13 *How many in the group?*

Having considered the requirements for ambient temperature and grouping we need to decide on the way the cable is to be installed. This is referred to as the reference method.

Reference method

The way in which the cable is installed will have an effect on the current carrying capacity of the cable, as a result of the cable's ability to dissipate heat. There are many different methods of installing cables and the first task is to select the method to be used for our circuit.

BS 7671, Appendix 4 contains information on the current carrying capacities of a large number of different types of cables. Most of these cables can be installed using a large number of different methods. To enable us to determine the current carrying capacity, a system of reference methods has been devised and these are contained in Table 4A2 of Appendix 4 in BS 7671.

To help in the decision we first need to consider the appropriate methods of installation for our cable and guidance on this is given in Table 4A1 of Appendix 4 in BS 7671. This identifies the types of conductors and cables and the appropriate installation methods for each one.

Reference to Table 4A1 shows that a sheathed multicore cable can be installed using any of the methods except installation on insulators, which, unsurprisingly, is the only acceptable installation method for bare live conductors.

The reference methods make an allowance for some of the installation conditions and so we do not have to apply rating factors for these providing we select the appropriate reference method for our cable installation.

Table 3.7 shows a sample of the reference method requirements for the installation of cables used in BS 7671. By using the appropriate method, determined from the description, the particular reference method can be determined and we then use this reference method when selecting the cable based upon the current carrying capacity.

We can see from Table 4A2 that a large number of installation methods are covered here and this will assist us in selecting the appropriate cable for our particular installation.

Having identified the method of installing cables there is one significant installation condition which has a profound effect on the selection process and that is thermal insulation.

Task

Before you continue with this chapter familiarize yourself with Table 4A1 in Appendix 4 of BS 7671.

Table 3.7 *Reference methods*

Installation method			Reference method to be used to determine current carrying capacity
Number	Example	Description	
2		Multicore cable in conduit in a thermally insulated wall with an inner skin having thermal conductance not less than 10W/m²kᶜ	A
3		Multicore cable direct in a thermally insulated wall with an inner skin having thermal conductance not less than 10W/m²kᶜ	A
4		Non sheathed cables in a conduit on a wooden or masonry wall or spaced less than 0.3 x conduit diameter from it	B
20		Single or multicore cables fixed on (clipped direct) or spaced less than 0.3 x cable diameter from a wooden or masonry wall	C

Task

Before you continue with this chapter familiarize yourself with Table 4A2 in Appendix 4 of BS 7671.

Thermal insulation

Thermal insulation is designed to retain heat within the building and so by its very nature it does not allow heat to escape. If a cable is installed in contact with thermal insulation it will be unable to dissipate the heat it produces to the same extent as it would in free air. Combining the cable's heat producing properties with the thermal insulation's heat retention properties causes a considerable problem for the designer.

We found earlier that some of the conditions for the installation of cables are dealt with by selecting an appropriate installation reference method. This includes cables in thermally insulated walls contained within conduit and when installed direct without a containment system.

Regulation 523.9 of BS 7671 details the requirements for cables installed in thermal insulation and begins with a statement that cables should preferably be installed in a location where they are not likely to be covered with thermal insulation. In practice this should always be considered as the preferable option and altering cable routes wherever possible to avoid thermal insulation is desirable.

The effect of cables contained in thermal insulation is reflected by the rating factors that are to be applied.

Table 3.8 *Rating factors for cables in thermal insulation*

Cable surrounded by thermal insulation	
Length within the insulation	**Derating factor**
50mm	0.88
100mm	0.78
200mm	0.63
400mm	0.51
≥ 500mm	0.5

We can see from the figures in Table 3.8 that the effect on the current carrying capacity can be quite serious. A cable run for 0.5m or more in thermal insulation will have its current carrying capacity effectively halved. In real terms this means that the cable will need to be at least twice the size we would otherwise need to use.

If cables have to be installed in thermal insulation then using one of the installation options given in the reference methods is the next consideration. For example, if we can install the cable within a containment system fixed as detailed in method number 2 or 3 then this will remove the need to apply a rating factor.

When it is not possible to avoid an area where the cable is to be surrounded by thermal insulation one option is to terminate the cable either side of the area and use the larger cable only where the thermal insulation is installed.

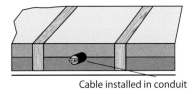
Cable installed in conduit

Figure 3.14 *Flat twin and cpc cable installed in thermal insulation*

It is important to realize that pvc cables directly in contact with some thermal insulation material will not only be affected by the heat produced, but also from a chemical reaction which may damage the cable. This is particularly so when in contact with polystyrene which was widely used as an insulation material. Care needs to be taken when carrying out installations in older properties as it was particularly popular as a retro-fit cavity wall insulation material.

There is a particular requirement for flat twin and earth cables installed in contact with thermal insulation.

Table 3.9 *Installation methods for flat twin and earth cable in thermal insulation*

Reference methods for flat twin and earth cables in thermal insulation			
Installation method			Reference method to be used to determine current carrying capacity
Number	Example	Description	
100		Clipped direct to a wooden joist, or touching the plaster-board ceiling surface, above a plasterboard ceiling with thermal insulation **not exceeding 100mm** in thickness having a minimum U value of 0.1W/m^{2}K	Table 4D5
101		Clipped direct to a wooden joist, or touching the plaster-board ceiling surface, above a plasterboard ceiling with thermal insulation **exceeding 100mm** in thickness having a minimum U value of 0.1W/m^{2}K	Table 4D5
102		In a stud wall with thermal insulation with a minimum U value 0.1W/m^{2}K with the **cable touching** the inner wall surface, or touching the plasterboard ceiling surface, and the inner skin having a minimum U value of 10W/m^{2}K	Table 4D5
103		In a stud wall with thermal insulation with a minimum U value 0.1W/m^{2}K with the cable **not touching** the inner wall surface	Table 4D5

There is a separate section which relates solely to flat twin and cpc cables and the current carrying capacities for these are given in a separate table. The information contained in BS 7671, Table 4C is shown in Table 3.9 above.

One more rating factor which we may need to apply is related to the type of protective device used to protect against overcurrent.

Type of overcurrent protection

Some kinds of protective devices operate when the circuit current exceeds their current rating by a relatively small amount. The relationship between I_n and the current required for the device to operate is referred to as the fusing factor. Where this fusing factor exceeds 1.45 an additional rating factor has to be applied. This is because it will take the device longer to operate under overload and so the conductor temperature may rise significantly.

Fortunately most of the protective devices in use have a fusing factor less than 1.45, however this is not the case for the BS 3036 semi-enclosed rewireable fuse.

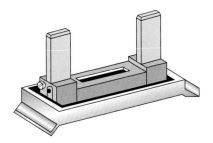

Figure 3.15 *BS 3036 semi-enclosed fuse*

The BS 3036 fuse has a fusing factor of around 2.0, so it requires twice the I_n value of the fuse element for it to disconnect. To compensate for this we need to apply a rating factor when we are selecting cables protected by this type of device.

The rating factor for this particular situation is a constant value and so there is no table required for the rating factor, which is 0.725, which is given in Regulation 433.1.101. The requirement given there is that the I_n of the fuse does not exceed $0.725 \times I_z$ for the lowest rated conductor protected.

Underground cables

So far we have looked at the rating factors which are applied to cables installed in premises. There are a number of rating factors which may apply to cables buried in the ground. We shall consider these briefly here as the application of the rating factors which may affect the current carrying capacity for buried cables.

The considerations are:

- buried cables
- depth of burial
- thermal resistivity of soil.

Buried cables

When cables are buried in the ground the first consideration is that the ambient temperature is lower and the ambient temperature tables are with a normal temperature of 20°C. Where the soil temperatures vary from this value the current carrying capacity needs to be adjusted. An exception is made where the soil temperature around the cables varies by no more than 5°C for a few weeks of the year.

Depth of burial

The cable ratings for buried cables are based upon a depth of 0.7m and where the depth varies from this then the current carrying capacity requires adjustment. As the depth of cable goes beyond 0.7m so the rating factor decreases. For example, a cable buried at 0.5m has a correction factor of 1.03 whilst a cable buried at 1.0m has a rating factor of 0.97.

Thermal resistivity

The cable rating factors are based upon a standard soil resistivity of 2.5K.m/W. Where the soil resistivity is higher than this the current carrying capacity of the cable should be reduced. This will require accurate measurements of soil resistivity around the cable. In extreme circumstances the soil immediately around the cable may be replaced with a more suitable material.

Task

Referring to BS 7671, record the rating factors and the table from which they were obtained for each of the following:

1 Rating factors for 70°C thermoplastic cables in ambient air temperatures other than 30.

BS 7671 Table:								
Temp °C	25	30	35	40	45	50	55	60	65
Factor								

2 Rating factors for grouping multicore cables.

BS 7671 Table:							
Bunched on a surface	Number of circuits of multicore cables						
	6	7	8	9	12	16	20
Factor							

Try this: Crossword

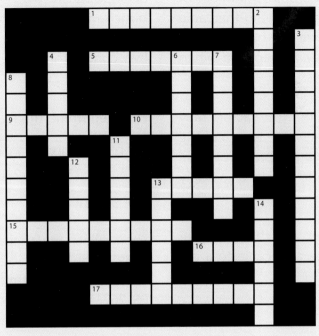

Across

1   Comes as a bolt from the blue? (9)

5   Hard but easily broken (7)

9   Derived from the sun as a type of energy (5)

10 This type of material will eat metal (9)

13 This often accompanies fauna outside (5)

15 If it has an effect it may be called an external one of these (9)

16 Fine dirt particles are .... (4)

17 A whole lot of shaking in this (9)

Down

2   Bunch them all together and we call it this (8)

3   This forms on cold glasses in a humid atmosphere (12)

4   Conductors and insulation form part of this (5)

6   When socks are this they keep your feet warm (7)

7   Too much of this in the sun can cause burns (8)

8   Wrapped around conductors to prevent shock (10)

11 If it is underground it is this (6)

12 Forms in dark, dank and damp places (5)

13 Used to determine I_t when working with I_n (6)

14 I_n is the current .... (6)

Part 4 Selecting live conductors

We have established that there are a number of rating factors which may apply during the cable selection process and now we need to put these together and see how they are applied when selecting the live conductors.

The first thing to realize is that the factors may not all apply throughout the whole length of the cable route. If all the factors are present at the same point in the cable route we need to apply all the factors.

Let's consider all the factors, and their designation symbols, which may be applicable to a circuit within a building:

● ambient temperature – C_a
● thermal insulation – C_i
● grouping – C_g
● BS 3036 fuse – C_f

These rating factors are applied to our cable selection process once we have selected the protective device rating I_n for the circuit we are to install. They are used as divisors to the I_n value and where the rating factors are less than 1, the minimum I_t value for the cable will be higher than the I_n of the protective device.

Example

A 9.0kW electric shower circuit is to be installed in a dwelling using 70°C flat twin and cpc, thermoplastic cable clipped direct to the building structure. The protective device is a BS EN 60898 type B circuit breaker and at one point in the cable route the cable is bunched with one other circuit in an ambient temperature of 35°C. Determine the cpc of the live conductors required to meet the requirements of BS 7671.

First determine the load current I_b:

$$I = \frac{P}{V} = \frac{9 \times 1000}{230} = \frac{9000}{230} = 39.13A$$

$I_b = 39.13A$

Then select the protective device. As a BS EN 60898 type B circuit breaker is to be used and the circuit is rated more than 32A we can use BS 7671, Table 41.3 to select a suitable device. The selection of the protective device must follow the rule $I_n \geq I_b$ and as $I_b = 39.13A$ then $I_n \geq 39.13A$. The protective device rating which is closest to and above the circuit design current is 45A.

$I_n = 40A$

To determine the minimum value of I_t the appropriate rating factors have to be applied to the I_n. So the rating factors are taken from BS 7671 and are:

● The ambient temperature is 35°C and the rating factor, taken from BS 7671 Table 4B1, gives a C_a of 0.94.
● The cable is not in contact with any thermal insulation so C_i is 1.0.
● The cable is grouped with one other circuit so the total number of circuits is two and using BS 7671, Table 4C1, Item 1, this gives a C_g of 0.8.

Task

Refer to BS 7671, Table 4B1 and check the figure for C_a.

Task

Refer to BS 7671, Table 4C1 and check the figure for C_g.

● As the protective device is a BS EN 60898 circuit breaker and the correction rating for the type of device is not applicable, this gives a C_f of 1.0.

As all of these conditions occur at the same point in the installation we must apply all the rating factors and these are applied to I_n.

$$\text{Minimum } I_t = \frac{I_n}{C_a \times C_i \times C_g \times C_f}$$

$$= \frac{40}{0.94 \times 1.0 \times 0.8 \times 1.0} = \frac{40}{0.752}$$

$$= 53.19A$$

Due to the installation conditions the current carrying capacity of the cable has increased.

Selecting the cable based upon the required current carrying capacity for a flat twin and cpc cable we refer to BS 7671, Table 4D5, column 6, as the cable is installed clipped direct.

The minimum cable we can use must have an $I_t \geq 53.19A$. The first cable which meets this requirement is a 10mm^2 with an I_t of 64A.

So we have selected the appropriate size of live conductors for our load current and installation conditions.

It is important to realize that the rating factors applied are those which create the worst conditions for the cable. This may be where a number

Task

Refer to BS 7671, Table 4D5, column 6 and check the cable selection.

Try this

A circuit to supply a 230V, 3kW, single-phase heater is to be installed using a flat twin and cpc cable clipped direct to the surface of the building. The protective device is a BS 88-3 fuse and the cable is grouped with two other cables in an ambient temperature of 30°C, the cable is not in contact with thermal insulation. Determine the csa of the cable to meet the requirements of BS 7671.

_____

_____

_____

_____

_____

of conditions exist simultaneously or where the single worst condition exists. This is best demonstrated by the use of some simple diagrams.

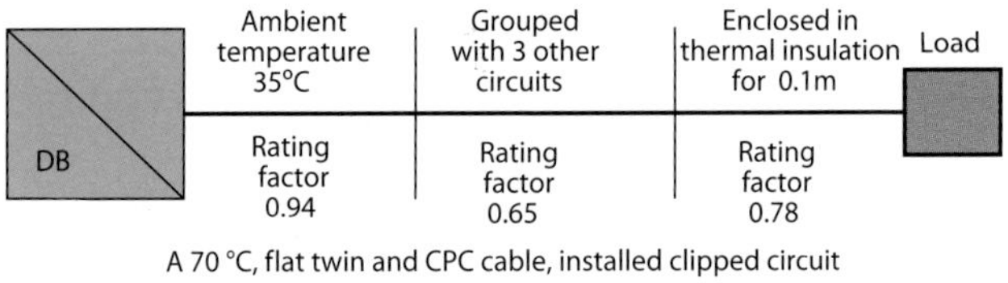

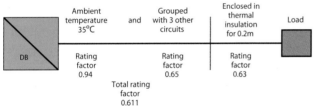

A 70 °C, flat twin and CPC cable, installed clipped circuit

Figure 3.16 *Rating factors along a cable route*

In Figure 3.16 we can see there are three different situations along the cable route. As they do not all appear together we use the lowest rating factor to determine the current carrying capacity of the cable. In this case it is the rating factor for the grouping of the cables at 0.65.

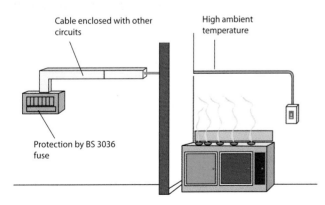

Figure 3.17 *Combined rating factors along a cable route*

In Figure 3.17 we have a situation where two conditions exist in the same place. For this example both the rating factors for ambient tempera-

ture will need to be applied to that part of the route, giving a total rating factor of 0.611. As this is lower than the 0.63 for the thermal insulation we use the 0.611 rating factor to determine the minimum current carrying capacity of the cable.

Remember

When calculating the current carrying capacity requirements we use the worst case scenario along the cable route to detemine the rating factor. If more than one condition exists at the same location we must apply all the rating factors for that location. These rating factors are multiplied together **not** added.

Diversity

We have considered the selection of a protective device based upon the load current of the circuit and this is carried out in every case except for a circuit supplying an electric cooker. For this circuit we can apply diversity to the load and this is only possible because of the way in which the cooker is used and the way in which the heating loads are controlled.

The requirements for cooking generally dictate that different parts of the cooker are switched on at different times and simmerstats and thermostats are constantly switching parts of the load on and off. So even if all the loads were switched on the temperature controls would have them switching on and off and the actual load would be less than the maximum.

The electric cooker is an exception to the general rule for these reasons and we can apply diversity as detailed in IET Guidance Note 1, Selection and Erection or the IET On-Site Guide.

Figure 3.18 *Different conditions along the route*

If we consider a domestic electric cooker with a total load of say 15kW, the chance of the whole load being switched on at the same time is somewhat remote. The total load is made up of a number of small loads all fitted with their own control. The controls are usually some form of temperature adjustment which allows the heating elements to switch on and off to maintain a temperature.

For domestic installations a calculation has been developed which allows for this diversity of the load on cookers.

It means that once the maximum load has been calculated the first 10A must be taken as being always there, then 30 per cent of the remaining current should be added to the 10A.

So for our 15kW cooker (power factor is unity for the heating load):

$$I = \frac{P}{V} = \frac{15000}{230} = 65.22A \text{ full load}$$

The load after diversity will be:

$$65.22A - 10A = 55.22A$$

We now take 30 per cent of this value and add it to the 10A and so we have:

$$55.22 \times \frac{30}{100} = 16.57A + 10A = 26.57A$$

Obviously the protective device and cable for this new assumed load is much smaller and cheaper than one for the maximum load.

It may be possible to apply diversity factors to other loads apart from cookers but great care must always be taken when designing the circuit. If it is possible to have the maximum load connected for any length of time a serious overload situation could occur.

It is more common to apply diversity to a complete installation or sections of an installation.

As we have seen it is not always necessary to supply all the electrical equipment within an electrical installation with full load current at the same moment in time. Indeed it is often quite unlikely that all the equipment will be loaded to a maximum at any one time.

The designer of an electrical installation may make some allowances for this fact when calculating the load for the installation and apply diversity.

The application of diversity to installations requires some considerable knowledge and understanding of the intended use of the installation and the type of equipment being used. Other final circuits supplying, for example, lighting in a domestic installation, have other allowances for diversity. These can be found in IET Guidance Note 1, Selection and Erection and the IET On-Site Guide.

It is common for the DNO to apply diversity when determining the supply cable and their protective devices for an installation. They will assume that all of the load will not be in use at the same time and make an application for diversity accordingly.

We have nearly completed the selection process for the live conductors but there is one more requirement we have to consider.

Task

Using the diversity tables in the IET ON-Site Guide or Guidance Note 1 determine the diversity allowance for:

a lighting loads in a small office building

b two electric cookers in a small guest house

c floor warming installation in a dwelling

Try this

A domestic flat requires a new main cable to supply it. As this is part of a larger installation, it is the responsibility of the consumer to supply the cable. The loads within the flat are:

Lighting   8 × 100W filament lamps and 2 × 80W fluorescent luminaires
Power   9 × 13A socket outlets connected to a single 32A ring final circuit
Cooker   18kW rated current
Water heater   1 × 3kW (instantaneous)

Calculate the assumed current demand for the flat which is supplied at 230V single-phase.

Voltage drop

When current passes through a resistance there is a voltage drop and this applies to the current flowing through a conductor. Although conductor resistances are generally very low there will still be some voltage drop across the length of the circuit. The factors which affect the voltage drop are:

- the resistance of the conductors
- the length of the conductors
- the current carried by the conductors.

When we selected the cable based on the current carrying capacity required we referred to the tables in BS 7671 Appendix 4. These tables also carry information related to the voltage drop for the cables and installation reference methods.

Table 4D1B gives the voltage drop for single core thermoplastic cables. The first thing to be aware of is that the values are given in millivolts per amp per meter (mV/A/m) and so those values need to be divided by 1000 to convert to volts.

Table 3.10 gives a sample of the mV/A/m for the single core, 70°C thermoplastic cables installed in a conduit or trunking taken from Table 4D1B column 6 in BS 7671. Once the conductor csa has been determined we can use the installation reference method and csa to establish the voltage drop in mV/A/m. We can then use this information to determine the actual voltage drop for the circuit.

Table 3.10 *Voltage drop for single core thermoplastic cable installed in conduit or trunking*

Voltage drop for single 70°C thermoplastic cables Methods A and B	
Conductor CSA in mm²	Voltage drop in mV/A/m
1.0	38
1.5	25
2.5	15
4.0	9.5
6.0	6.4
10	3.8
16	2.4

Example:

A power circuit is to be installed using 2.5mm², single core 70°C thermoplastic cables contained in a plastic trunking. The load current is 25A, ac single-phase and the length of the circuit is 40m. Determine whether the cable selection meets the requirements for voltage drop constraint.

The calculation to work out the voltage drop is:

$$\text{Voltage drop} = \frac{\text{mV/A/m} \times I_b \times 1}{1000}$$

In this example mV/A/m = 15mV, I_b = 25A and length (l) = 40m.

$$\text{So Voltage drop} = \frac{15 \times 25 \times 40}{1000} = \frac{15000}{1000} = 15V$$

Task

Before you continue with this chapter familiarize yourself with Table 4D1B, in Appendix 4 of BS 7671.

Having established the actual voltage drop for this circuit we need to determine whether or not this complies with the voltage drop constraints.

The main requirement for voltage drop is that the voltage at the terminals of all equipment should meet the manufacturer's requirements and not affect the efficiency or operation of the equipment. BS 7671 requires that, in the absence of such information, the installation is deemed to meet the requirements providing the voltage drop from the origin of the installation to the furthest point on any circuit does not exceed certain values.

The maximum values of voltage drop are given in Table 4Ab of Appendix 4 in BS 7671.

If we consider the figures in Table 3.11 for our example we can see that, as a power circuit, a maximum of 5 per cent is acceptable.

Table 3.11 *Maximum voltage drop for low voltage installations taken from BS 7671*

Voltage drop		
Low voltage installations	Lighting	Other circuits
Supplied from a public DNO	3%	5%
Supplied from a private source	6%	8%

Five per cent of 230V is 11.5 Volts and for the circuit in our example we have a volt drop of 15 volts so it does not comply.

To overcome the problem of a voltage drop which is too high we have a number of options:

● reduce the load current
● reduce the length of the run
● use a larger conductor.

The first two of these are generally not possible and so we are left with increasing the conductor csa.

If we select the next csa of conductor (in this case it will be a 4mm^2 conductor) we have a volt drop of 9.5mV/A/m. Using our volt drop calculation formula we have a new voltage drop of:

$$\text{Voltage drop} = \frac{9.5 \times 25 \times 40}{1000} = \frac{9500}{1000} = 9.5\text{V}$$

And as 9.5V ≤ 11.5V the circuit will now comply.

We may have to carry out this calculation a number of times in order to find a cable that meets the criteria. To save a lot of work we can rearrange the formula to calculate the maximum mV/A/m we could have for our circuit. If our selected cable is ≤ the calculated value it will comply. If it is not then we go further down the mV/A/m table until we find the first acceptable value and then select the csa to correspond.

Example:

A power circuit operating at 230V single-phase with a load current of 25A is installed using a thermoplastic steel wire armoured cable clipped direct and a length of run of 55m, is protected by a BS 88-2 fuse and no rating factors are

Task
Before you continue with this chapter familiarize yourself with Table 4D1B, in Appendix 4 of BS 7671.

applicable. The rating of the protective device is going to be 25A (see Table 41.4 in BS 7671) and with no rating factors to be applied (they are all =1) the minimum csa of conductor for this circuit is 2.5mm^2 with an I_t rated at 28A.

We know the maximum voltage drop allowed is 11.5 Volts. If we put this into our formula we get:

$$11.5V = \frac{mV/A/m \times 25 \times 55}{1000}$$
$$= \text{so rearranged } \frac{11.5V \times 1000}{25 \times 55}$$
$$= \text{Maximum } mV/A/m$$
$$= 8.36 \, mV/A/m$$

The cable is thermoplastic armoured, clipped to the surface and single-phase so we refer to Table 4D4B in Appendix 4 of BS 7671 and look for the first cable having a mV/A/m ≤ 8.36. In this case it will be 6mm^2 cable with 7.3mV/A/m. A check in Table 4D4A shows that the current carrying capacity for this cable is 49A in the conditions given.

It is important to remember that the voltage drop is taken from the incoming supply terminals to the farthest point in the circuit and the voltage drop for a particular circuit may only be a part of the total acceptable voltage drop. Figure 3.19 shows a situation where the circuit forms part of a complex installation supplied by two distribution circuits. The distribution circuits will also produce a volt drop and this must be taken into account when carrying out the voltage drop calculation for the circuit.

Each distribution circuit in Figure 3.19 has resulted in a voltage drop of 3.06 volts and so a total of 6.12 volts to the final distribution board. This means the final circuit will have a maximum permitted voltage drop of 11.5V – 6.12V = 5.38V in order to meet the requirements.

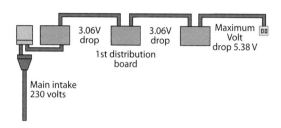

Figure 3.19 *Voltage drop in a complex system*

Each distribution circuit will have an effect on the voltage drop for the next stage of the installation. It is often advisable to keep the voltage drop to a minimum in the distribution cables (larger csa) to keep the final circuit conductors to a manageable size. Installing a lighting circuit where 4 mm^2 cables have to be used to comply with the voltage drop requirements can be difficult as the standard fittings will not accept conductors of this size.

These voltage drop calculations have shown that, whilst we first need to determine the required current carrying capacity of the conductors, it is often the voltage drop constraint that finally determines the conductor csa.

Task

Refer to BS 7671, Table 4D4A and 4D4B to check the cable selection.

Try this

A new circuit is to be installed to supply a 230V, 7kW single-phase kiln. The cable is to be a 3 core, SWA with 70°C thermoplastic insulation and copper conductors. One conductor is to be used as the cpc and the protective device is a BS EN 60898 type C circuit breaker. The length of the circuit is 30m and the cable is to be run clipped direct to the building structure separate from other cables in an ambient temperature of 35°C. Determine the minimum cross-sectional area of live conductors, for both current carrying capacity and voltage drop, for the circuit.

Part 5 Shock risk and thermal constraints

Having selected the live conductors for the circuits we are going to install we must now consider whether our circuit will meet the requirements for shock risk and thermal constraints.

Shock risk

Where an overcurrent device such as a fuse or circuit breaker is to be used to provide fault protection using automatic disconnection of supply (ADS) we must ensure that disconnection will occur automatically within the required time.

In the previous chapters of this study guide we established the earth fault loop paths and the effect these would have on the current flowing in the event of a fault to earth.

Remember

The earth fault loop path for a system is determined by $Z_s = Z_e + (R_1 + R_2)$.

It will be necessary to determine the impedance of the earth fault loop path for the circuit we are installing and for this we need to know the external earth fault loop impedance and the resistance of the line and cpc conductors of the circuit. Let's consider the requirements using an example.

Example:

A circuit to supply a 230V, 3kW, single-phase load is to be installed using a flat twin and cpc cable clipped direct to the surface of the building. The protective device is a BS EN 60898 type B circuit breaker and the cable is grouped with two other cables in an ambient temperature of 30°C. The cable is not in contact with thermal insulation and the length of the circuit is 25m. The supply system is TN-S and the Z_e for the installation is 0.3Ω. Determine the csa of the cable to meet the all requirements of BS 7671.

So from our previous calculations we can determine that:

- I_b = 13.04A
- I_n = 16A,
- minimum I_t = 22.86A
- csa = 2.5mm^2
- mV/A/m = 18mV
- calculated volt drop = 5.87V
- maximum permitted voltage drop = 11.5V.

and that so far the circuit complies with the requirements.

We now need to confirm the provision of shock protection and we know that Ze is 0.3Ω and we need to determine the resistance of R_1 and R_2. IET Guidance Notes 1, Selection and Erection and Guidance Notes 3, Inspection and Testing provide details of the resistance of conductors. In GN1 the information is contained in Table E1 in Appendix E, and in GN3 it is in Table A1 in Appendix A.

The resistance of 2.5mm^2 conductors and their associated protective conductors are shown in Table 3.12.

Table 3.12 *Resistance of conductors at 20°C*

Resistance of copper conductors in mΩ/m		
CSA in mm^2	CSA in mm^2	Resistance at 20°C
Line conductor	Protective conductor	$R_1 + R_2$
2.5	–	7.41
2.5	1.0	25.51
2.5	1.5	19.51
2.5	2.5	14.82

There are several important features to note in this table:

1 The resistance of the conductors is given in milliohms per metre and we must remember to divide these figures by 1000 to give values in ohms.
2 The resistances quoted are at 20°C which is generally the temperature taken at the time of testing.

The standard arrangement for a 2.5mm^2 flat twin and cpc cable is for a 1.5mm^2 cpc.

To calculate the resistance of the line and cpc conductors we use the row with the 2.5mm^2 line and 1.5mm^2 cpc to arrive at a figure of 19.51mΩ/m as the resistance of both conductors added together ($R_1 + R_2$). We know the circuit is 25m long and that Z_e is 0.3Ω so we have most of the information we need to determine the resistance of the earth fault path.

It is important here to remember that the figures for ($R_1 + R_2$) are given at 20°C which will **not** be the temperature when the circuit is operating and carrying load current. We need to consider the resistance of the cables at normal operating temperature. For this cable the normal operating temperature is 70°C and so we have to introduce a multiplying factor for this condition. This multiplier is a constant of 1.2 and has no units. This will increase the calculated resistance to compensate for the increase in conductor resistance when the cables are at normal operating temperature.

We can now calculate the Z_s for the circuit:

$$Z_s = Z_e + \frac{((R_1 + R_2) \times 25m \times 1.2))}{1000}$$

$$= 0.3 + \frac{(19.51 \times 25 \times 1.2)}{1000}$$

$$= 0.3 + \frac{585.3}{1000} = 0.885\Omega$$

So Z_s for our circuit is 0.885Ω.

Once again we need to refer to information in BS 7671 to determine whether this Z_s value will provide disconnection within the required time. The tables contained in Chapter 41 of BS 7671 provide details of the maximum values for Z_s if the disconnection time is to be achieved. As we

compensated for the increase in conductor temperature when we calculated the Z_s value we can compare directly with the tables in BS 7671.

The circuit is rated less than 32A and forms part of a TN-S system and therefore the disconnection time has to be within 0.4 seconds.

If we refer to Table 41.3 in Chapter 41 of BS 7671 we see that the maximum Z_s for the 16 A BS EN 60898 type B circuit breaker is 2.87Ω. The Z_s for the circuit must be equal to or less than the maximum tabulated value in BS 7671 and $0.885\Omega < 2.87\Omega$ so the circuit complies.

Remember

We can compare the calculated Z_s value directly with the maximum tabulated value in BS 7671 only because we have compensated for the temperature difference using the 1.2 multiplier in the calculation.

Try this

A 30m final circuit is installed using single core, thermoplastic insulated, copper conductors protected by a BS EN 60898 type C circuit breaker. The load current I_b is 40A and as no rating factors are to be applied the protective device I_n is also 40A. The csa of the live conductors has been determined as 6.0mm^2 using installation. Reference Method B and a 4.0mm^2 cpc has been installed. Ze = 0.34Ω and the conductor resistances at 20°C are 6mm^2 = 3.08mΩ/m and 4.0mm^2 = 4.61mΩ/m. Using the information in the tables in BS 7671 determine whether the circuit earth fault loop impedance will meet the requirements for automatic disconnection.

Thermal constraints

Having selected the conductors to meet the requirements of the load current, voltage drop and for shock protection we now have to consider the effects on the conductors in the event of a fault. Should a fault to earth occur then a high current will flow for the period of time required for the protective device to operate. The compliance with the thermal constraints is to verify that the conductors and insulation and surrounding material will not be damaged due to the current flow in the event of a fault.

The circuit protective conductor is generally a smaller cross-sectional area than the live conductors, and the current that it carries may be quite high, so a great deal of heat will be generated whilst the current flows. If sufficient current flows for long enough the heat produced could be such that the insulation catches fire. Once this happens disconnection of the supply will not extinguish the flames.

To prevent this situation occurring we must ensure that the circuit protective conductor is large enough to carry the fault current for the period of time needed for the device to disconnect the supply without excessive heat being produced.

The thermal constraint placed on the circuit by BS 7671 ensures that the cpc of the circuit is large enough to carry the earth fault current without a detrimental effect on the conductor, the insulation or the installation.

In order to find the minimum cross-sectional area of the circuit protective conductor we require the following information:

- the prospective earth fault current (I_f)
- the time taken for the protective device to operate with this fault current (t)

- the constant k which is related to the type of circuit protective conductor and its method of installation.

The way in which these are related to the minimum size of the circuit protective conductor is by a formula known as the adiabatic equation.

The minimum cross-sectional area of the conductor is referred to as 'S' and the formula we use is:

$$S = \frac{\sqrt{I^2 \times t}}{k} : \text{where I is the value of fault current } I_f$$

Note
It is important that the calculation is carried out in the right order to give the correct answer.

Let's consider the circuit supplying the electric load in our previous example to see if it complies with the requirements for thermal constraints.

We can determine the earth fault current as we have the U_0 value of 230V and a Z_s value of 0.885Ω. The earth fault current will be:

$$I_f = \frac{U_0}{Z_s} = \frac{230}{0.885} = 259.88A$$

As the protective device for this circuit is a BS EN 60898 type B circuit breaker we can check to determine the disconnection time for the circuit. When we confirmed the earth fault loop impedance for the circuit was acceptable we established that disconnection would be achieved within 0.1 to 5 seconds using the table in BS 7671 Chapter 41.

To confirm compliance with thermal constraints we need be more precise with the disconnection time for the circuit. For this we need to refer to the time/current curve information contained in BS 7671, Appendix 3.

We looked at the time/current characteristics briefly in the previous chapter but we need to consider them here in more detail.

Now that we know the value of the prospective fault current, we can further check the compliance of the circuit by using the tables in Appendix 3 of BS 7671. These tables are the simplified time/current curves for the various types of protective devices.

The horizontal axis is the prospective fault current and the vertical axis is the time. The divisions along the axis are logarithmic and so the divisions are not equal in size. Figure 3.20 shows a section of the X (horizontal) axis of the graph. The origin of the axis, the extreme left-hand end, has a value of 1 **not** 0 and the divisions go up in units of one until they reach 10. The divisions then go up in units of 10 until a value of 100 is reached at which point the divisions go up in units of 100 and so on. In this way a considerable current range can be covered in a relatively small space.

Figure 3.20 *The horizontal axis is the prospective fault current*

Figure 3.21 shows a section of the X axis where we have subdivided one of the sections. We must

remember that subdivisions of scale sections must be done in the same ratio as the main scale. This means that the value 250A is **not** going to be halfway between 200A and 300A. It occurs at a point approximately 0.66 of the way between these two as shown in Figure 3.21.

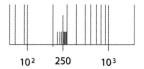

Figure 3.21 *The value 250 is not halfway between 200 and 300 but nearer two-thirds*

The vertical Y axis is shown in Figure 3.22 and again the origin of the axis is **not** 0. For ease of location the 1 second position is highlighted

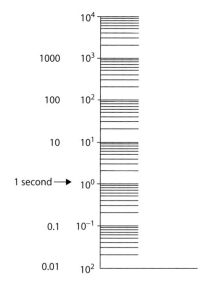

Figure 3.22 *The vertical axis is for the time in seconds*

 Try this

Mark the positions of the following currents on the current axis.

6A, 550A, 65A, 1250A and 275A

Task

Refer to Figure 3A4 in BS 7671 and determine the disconnection time for the 16A BS EN Type B circuit breaker when 259.88A flows.

on the axis in Figure 3.22. By working back down the axis we can see that the origin of the axis is in fact 0.01 seconds. Like the X axis the divisions are logarithmic and so the same proportional division of the scale must be used.

Now to further check the compliance of our circuit we can use the value of I_f and the appropriate time/current curve to establish the disconnection time for the device.

For our example the 16A, BS EN 60898, type B characteristics are given in BS 7671, Appendix 3, Figure 3A4.

We can see from the time/current curve that the fault current of 259.88A (using 250A as the closest point) occurs considerably after the vertical line down to 0.1s for the 16A device. This means that we can take the disconnection time as 0.1 seconds.

Note

The inset table in the BS 7671, Appendix 3 graphs, shows the fault current which is required to cause a protective device to operate within the required time (I_a). In the example a 16A BS EN 60898 Type B circuit breaker requires 80A to disconnect within 0.1 seconds.

Try this

Mark the positions of the following times on the time axis.

1.0s, 0.4s, 5.0s, 0.75s, 1.4s

Figure 3.23

Task

Familiarize yourself with Tables 54.2 to 54.7 in BS 7671 before continuing with this chapter.

Having determined the disconnection time we need to find the value of the constant k for our circuit.

The values for k are given in Tables 54.2 to 54.7 in BS 7671. At the head of each table is the description of the method of installation of the circuit protective conductor.

For our type of cable and method of installation (bunched with cables) we find the value of k to be 115 from Table 54.3 (70°C thermoplastic, copper < 300mm^2).

We can now put all the values into the formula to determine the minimum csa for the protective conductor:

$$S = \frac{\sqrt{I^2 \times t}}{k} = \frac{\sqrt{259.88^2 \times 0.1}}{115}$$

$$= \frac{\sqrt{6753.76}}{115} = \frac{82.18}{115} = 0.714 \, \text{mm}^2$$

We must carry out the calculation in the correct sequence to give the correct solution:

Stage one:	square the value of I_f ($I_f \times I_f$)
Stage two:	multiply the result by the time t second
Stage three:	take the square root of the result
Stage four:	divide the answer by the value of k

As the minimum size of cpc to give compliance is 1.08mm^2 and we have installed a cpc of 4.0mm^2 we can see that circuit fulfils the requirements for thermal constraints and so our circuit complies.

If the size of cpc installed proves to be insufficient then a larger cross-sectional area conductor must be used. This will, of course, have an effect on the value of the earth fault loop impedance as a larger cpc will reduce the impedance and a higher current will flow. This in turn will reduce the disconnection time.

We could calculate the minimum requirements based on the known criteria that apply to our circuit. For example if we know the maximum disconnection time and the type and rating of the protective device we can establish the minimum value of I_f to achieve the required disconnection time. This data and the value of k for the type of cpc and its method of installation will allow us to establish the minimum size of cpc to give compliance under the worst conditions.

For this calculation we must use the minimum value of I_f to give the disconnection time required, the maximum disconnection time and k for the type and method of cpc installation. If we carry out this one calculation we can establish the minimum size of cpc to comply with the absolute worst conditions and we can ensure that the size selected will be within a usable range.

This can be particularly useful when designing circuits for installation in conduit and trunking where the size of cpc can be varied with ease. It will also ensure that a great deal of time is not wasted carrying out repeated calculations to establish an acceptable size.

Task

Using Table 54.3 from BS 7671 complete the details below for conductors less than 300mm².

Values of k for protective conductors as a core in a cable or bunched with cables			
	Insulation material		
Conductor material	70°C Thermoplastic	90°C Thermoplastic	90°C Thermosetting
Copper			
Aluminium			

Try this

A 230V single-phase circuit is to supply an industrial heater with a load of 27A and which forms part of a TN-S system. The cable is to be a thermoplastic single insulated installed in plastic conduit with 6mm² live conductors and a 4mm² cpc to a location 25m from the supply intake position and no factors need to be applied. It is protected by a BSEN 60898 type C circuit breaker and Ze is 0.4Ω. Determine the minimum size of cpc that could be installed to comply with the requirements for thermal constraints.

Part 6 Capacities of conduit and trunking

Installing cables

When working out the capacity of an enclosure such as conduit or trunking there are two important requirements to be considered:

- when we install cables we must ensure that no damage is done to the conductor, its insulation or the enclosure itself
- there must be sufficient space for air to circulate around the cables once they have been installed.

> **Remember**
> The current-carrying capacity of a cable will be affected if it is grouped or bunched with other cables.

The standard method of determining the capacity of conduit and trunking works on unit basis and applying the requirements will ensure that the requirements are met.

The unit basis applies a factor to the:

- capacity of the containment system based upon the available area
- the conductors which are to be installed.

These factors are available in IET Guidance Note 1, Selection and Erection (GN1) and the IET On-Site Guide and are based on the standard sizes of cables and enclosures.

Cable factors

There are three sets of cable factors given in GN1 these being cable factors for cables:

- installed in trunking
- in short straight conduit runs
- in long conduit runs (> 3m) and runs of any length incorporating bends.

Cables installed in trunking are less prone to installation damage as the trunking has one open side to allow cables to be laid into the trunking. Conduits require the cables to be pulled into the conduit between draw in points which puts tensile force on the conductors and abrasive and heat forces on the insulation. Long runs of conduit and bends and sets in the conduit increase these forces. As a result of these varied installation conditions the factors alter to compensate for the conditions.

Cables in trunking

In Table A5 of Guidance Note 1 the factor given for solid and stranded cables is different, for example, the factor given for a solid 1.5mm^2 thermoplastic conductor is 8.0 while that for a stranded 1.5mm^2 thermoplastic conductor is 8.6. This is due to the overall diameter of a stranded conductor being larger than a solid conductor of the same cross-sectional area. These factors are used to determine trunking capacity and in themselves have no units.

Task
Before continuing with this chapter locate Table A5 in Appendix 5 of GN1.

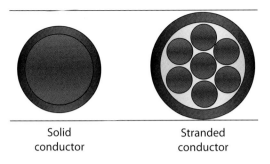

Solid conductor   Stranded conductor

Figure 3.24 *Comparison of overall diameters of solid and stranded conductors*

The remainder of Table A.5 provides the cable factors for the different csa of thermoplastic and thermosetting single core conductors.

If we now refer to Table A.6, the factors for trunking are provided there. For example, a 50mm × 50mm trunking has a factor of 1037 whilst the factor for a 75mm × 25mm trunking is 738. These factors are relative to the area available for cable and also have no units.

Care must be taken to use the correct factor for the type of cable that is to be installed.

Example:

A number of 1.5mm^2 stranded thermoplastic conductors are to be installed in a trunking. The proposed trunking size is 50mm × 50mm and we need to determine the maximum number of cables that could be installed, and if three conductors are required for each circuit how many circuits can be accommodated.

Factor for 50mm × 50mm trunking = 1037

Factor for 1 × 1.5mm^2 stranded cable = 8.6

Maximum number of cables we could install

$$\frac{\text{Trunking factor}}{\text{Cable factor}} = \frac{1037}{8.6} = 120.58$$

As we cannot use fractions of cables the maximum number is 120 cables. If three conductors

are required for each circuit the maximum number of circuits we can install is:

$$\frac{120}{3} = 40 \text{ circuits.}$$

This is a quick method of working out capacities of trunking but we can only use it for standard sizes. We shall now apply this method to a typical installation problem.

Example:

A 75mm × 25mm trunking is installed and contains 26 × 2.5mm^2 stranded cables and 20 × 4mm^2 cables. We are to install some extra circuits which will total 12 × 1.5mm^2 solid copper cables. Does the trunking have enough capacity for these extra cables?

Using GN1 the factors are:

75mm × 25mm = 738
2.5mm^2 stranded cable = 12.6
4mm^2 stranded cable = 16.6
1.5mm^2 stranded cable = 8.0

Total factor for 2.5mm^2 stranded cables = 26 × 12.6 = 327.6

Total factor for 4mm^2 cables = 20 × 16.6 = 332

Total factor for installed cables = 327.6 + 332 = 659.6

Trunking factor for 75mm × 25mm = 738

Factor available for extra cables:

Trunking factor – total factor for installed cables = 738 – 659.6 = 78.4

Factor for 1.5mm^2 solid copper cable = 8.0

Number of extra cables we could install:

$$\frac{78.4}{8.0} = 9.8 \text{ so we could only install 9 extra cables}$$

Therefore our trunking has not got sufficient capacity to allow us to install 12 more 1.5mm^2 solid core cables.

Try this

1 Using the factors given in IET Guidance Note 1 determine how many 6mm^2 thermosetting cables could be installed in a 75mm × 38mm trunking.

2 Determine the minimum size of trunking that will be required to install the following cables:

4 × 6mm^2 flexible thermoplastic

12 × 4mm^2 flexible thermosetting

30 × 2.5mm^2 stranded thermoplastic

36 × 1.5mm^2 stranded thermosetting

Space factor for trunking

If we are to use trunking containment systems which are a different size to those listed in the tables, we need to use a space factor calculation. The space factor considers the amount of space available within an enclosure that may be filled with cables to ensure we comply with the points listed earlier.

The maximum value of trunking space factor is 45 per cent. This means that only 45 per cent of

the available space may be cables, so 55 per cent must be air space.

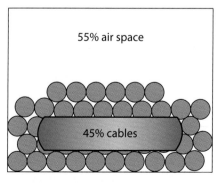

Figure 3.25 *Space factor for trunking*

Example:

Remember that the space occupied by cables includes the insulation, so we cannot use the conductor size (such as 2.5mm²) as this does not include the insulation. Therefore we have to measure the diameter of the cable, including the insulation, and calculate its total area.

To find out how many cables of overall diameter 3mm we can install in a 50mm × 50mm steel trunking we need to carry out the calculation:

Total area of trunking = $50 \times 50 = 2500\text{mm}^2$

Space available for cables (45%) = $2500 \times \dfrac{45}{100} = 1125\text{mm}^2$

This leaves $2500-1125 = 1375\text{mm}^2$ of air space within the trunking.

Space occupied by one cable = $\dfrac{\pi d^2}{4} = \dfrac{\pi \times 3^2}{4} = 7.07\text{mm}^2$

The maximum number of these cables we can install =

$$\frac{\text{space available for cables}}{\text{space occupied by 1 cable}} = \frac{1125}{7.07} = 159.12$$

The maximum number of these cables we could install in a 50mm × 50mm trunking is 159.

If we needed to install conductors of different sizes we would have to do a lot of measuring and calculating to work out the capacities of our enclosures. Therefore, we would usually only use this method for non-standard sizes of cable or enclosure. For standard sizes we can use the factor tables.

Remember

The effective cross-sectional area of a non-circular cable is taken as that of a circle of diameter equal to the major axis of the cable.

Try this

Determine the number of insulated conductors with an overall diameter of 3.2mm² that can be installed in a 60mm x 60mm trunking.

Cables in conduit

We can use similar methods to work out the capacity of conduits. However, before we begin we need to clarify some of the factors used with the tables given in IET Guidance Note 1.

There are two sets of cable factors given in GN1, these being cable factors for cables:

- in short straight conduit runs
- in long conduit runs (> 3m) and runs of any length incorporating bends.

A short straight run is between draw in points – not the total length of conduit used. Any point where cables can be drawn in or out of the system can be described as a draw in point and can have a maximum distance between them of 3m to qualify for this factor.

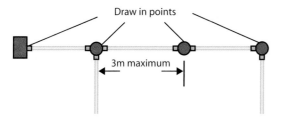

Figure 3.26 *Draw in points on a conduit system*

A bend is taken to be a 90° bend to the appropriate radius, and we assume that two sets of 45° are equal to one 90° bend and so on.

IET Guidance Note 1 contains tables of factors for conduit:

A1 – cables installed in short straight runs

A2 – conduits installed in short straight runs

A3 – cables installed in runs over 3m or containing bends and sets

A4 – conduits installed in runs over 3m or containing bends and sets.

For short straight runs of conduit the capacity can be worked out in the same way as for trunking.

Example:

How many 1.5mm^2 cables can be installed in a 20mm conduit when the conductors are:

a   solid

b   stranded?

Conduit factor for 20mm = 460

Cable factor for 1.5mm^2 solid = 27

Maximum number of solid cables =

$$\frac{\text{Conduit factor}}{\text{Cable factor}} = \frac{460}{27} = 17 \text{ cables}$$

Cable factor for 1.5mm^2 stranded = 31

Maximum number of stranded cables =

$$\frac{\text{Conduit factor}}{\text{Cable factor}} = \frac{460}{31} = 14 \text{ cables}$$

The use of solid conductors will allow three more cables to be installed than if the conductors were stranded.

When we install conduit it is inevitable that there will be locations where we have bends or sets.

Task

Before continuing with this chapter locate Tables A.1 and A.2 in Appendix 5 of GN1.

Task

Before continuing with this chapter locate Table A.4 in Appendix 5 of GN1.

Table A.4 provides the factors for runs incorporating bends and long straight runs and this table for conduit factors is different from those we have used so far. It is arranged in a grid with length of run down the left-hand side and the number of bends across the top.

Remember that the length of run is between draw in points. We can divide up a conduit run into shorter lengths with fewer bends by installing more draw in boxes. It is also worth considering that the use of an angle box can provide another draw in point and remove a 90° bend as shown in Figures 3.27 and 3.28.

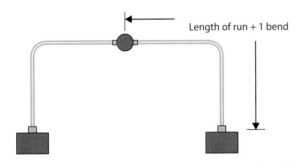

Figure 3.27 *Length of run and one 90° bend*

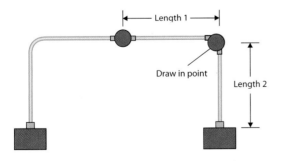

Figure 3.28 *Length reduced and bend removed with an angle box*

The examples that we shall consider will have the length of run stated between draw in points, so no further draw in points will be added.

Let's begin by looking at a 2m run of 20mm conduit with one 90° bend and see how many 1.5mm² cables we can install in it. You will notice that the table for cable factors in this case does not distinguish between solid and stranded conductors.

Conduit factor: Refer to Table A.4 in GN1 and look down the left-hand column until we find the 2.5m length of run. Follow this across to the block of vertical columns for one bend and select the column for 20mm conduit.

Where these two columns cross we have a factor of 278.

Cable factor: Referring to Table A.3 in GN1 the cable factor for a 1.5mm² is 22.

Maximum number of cables we can install =

$$\frac{\text{Conduit factor}}{\text{Cable factor}} = \frac{278}{22} = 12.6 \text{ cables}$$

So a maximum of 12 cables can be installed.

A typical installation problem may involve a route which has bends and sets which cannot be replaced by draw in boxes.

Example:

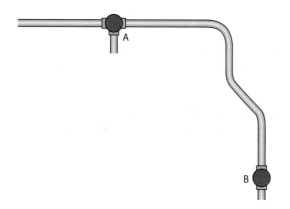

Figure 3.29 *Conduit run with equivalent of two 90° bends*

The 2.5m length of conduit between A and B in Figure 3.29 is to contain:

- 6 × 1.0mm² cables
  and
- 6 × 2.5mm² cables

Using the factors from GN1 determine the minimum size of conduit that can be used.

Cable factors

6 × 1.0mm² 6 × 16 = 96

6 × 2.5mm² 6 × 30 = 180

Total factor 96 + 180 = 276

Conduit factors

Length of run = 2.5m

Number of bends: 1 × 90° and 2 × 45° sets so it is equivalent to 2 × 90° bends.

Using Table A.4 with a length of 2.5m and the columns for two bends we must find a factor of 276 or more.

- 20mm has a factor of 244 and so is too small.
- 25mm has a factor of 442 and this is the one we must use.

A 25mm conduit is the smallest that could be installed.

Inspecting the tables for conduit factors shows that as the length of run or the number of bends increases the factor gets smaller, so the more complex the run the fewer cables we can install.

The blank squares in the bottom right-hand corner of the table are because using that length of run and number of bends it is impractical to pull cables through. In such a case we would need to split the run up by adding more draw in points. An example of how this is done is shown in Figures 3.30 and 3.31.

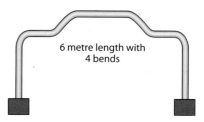

6 metre length with 4 bends

Figure 3.30 *Conduit with 6m length and four bends*

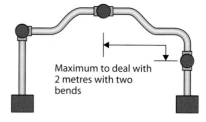

Maximum to deal with 2 metres with two bends

Figure 3.31 *Conduit redesigned to give a maximum 2m length with two bends*

So in practical situations planning the layout with a little care can reduce cost, time and size and make the installation easier.

Space factor for conduit

We considered the application of space factor for trunking earlier in this chapter. The application to conduit is not dissimilar. You should never

Figure 3.32 *Do not try to pull too many cables into an enclosure!*

attempt to pull too many cables into any enclosure because this could result in damage to the insulation and conductors. The space factor used to calculate how many cables can be pulled into a conduit is subsequently smaller.

Where the conduit is not a standard size given in the GN1 tables then the space factor for conduit is 35 per cent which means that the cables should not occupy more than 35 per cent of the available space within the conduit.

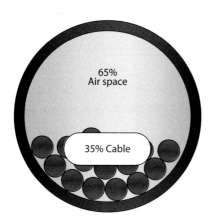

Figure 3.33 *Conduit space factor*

Conduit sizes represent the outside diameter of the conduit so a 20mm conduit has a 20mm outside diameter.

There are two important considerations when applying this space factor:

- the inside diameter must be used to calculate the area of the conduit
- the overall diameter of the cable, including insulation, must be used to calculate the conductor area.

Example

If we applied the 35% to a conduit with an inside diameter of 17.5mm

The space available for cables will be $\dfrac{\pi d^2}{4} = \dfrac{\pi \times 17.5^2}{4} = 240 \times \dfrac{35}{100} = 84\text{mm}^2$

Overall diameter of 1 cable including insulation = 2.9mm

Overall csa of 1 cable $\dfrac{\pi d^2}{4} = \dfrac{\pi \times 2.9^2}{4} = 6.6\text{mm}^2$

Maximum number of cables $= \dfrac{84}{6.6} = 12$ cables

Remember

To use the space factor the overall cross-sectional area of the cable including the insulation must be used.

You cannot use 1mm^2, 2.5mm^2 and so on because these refer to the conductor only. The effective cross-sectional area of a non-circular cable is taken as that of a circle of diameter equal to the major axis of the cable.

Try this

1   Determine the number of 2.5mm^2 cables that can be installed in a 25mm conduit which is 2m long and has two 90° bends.

2   The conduit run shown in Figure 3.34 contains 8 × 2.5mm^2 cables and you have to install a further 8 × 2.5mm^2 cables to supply extra circuits. Determine whether there is sufficient capacity to allow this.

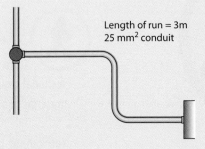

Length of run = 3m
25 mm^2 conduit

Figure 3.34

Try this: Crossword

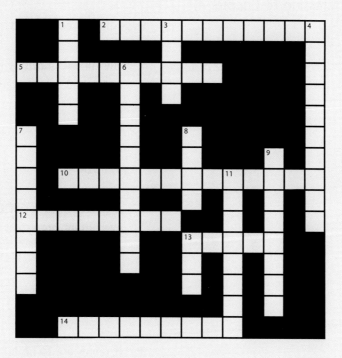

Across

2 The time/current graphs are this (11)

5 This is provided by overcurrent devices (10)

10 Overcurrent devices need to do this within a specific time (13)

12 Where the installation is placed (8)

13 The amount of room in a trunking (5)

14 When not all the loads are to be used we can apply this (9)

Down

1 A breakdown in insulation may result in this for a person (5)

3 The time and prospective fault current in the graphs are laid out along one of these (4)

4 When it meets the requirements it is said to be in............ (10)

6 When having to adjust for conditions we apply this type of factor (10)

7 Too much current in a healthy circuit is an....... (8)

8 Change of direction in a conduit is one of these (4)

9 The outside measurement of a conduit is its..... (8)

11 The number of cables that can be fitted in a trunking is the trunking....... (8)

13 Not quite a full bend in a conduit (3)

Congratulations, you have now completed Chapter 3 of this study guide. Complete the self assessment questions before progressing to Chapter 4.

SELF ASSESSMENT

Circle the correct answers.

1   The current drawn by a 9.2kW load with a power factor of 0.8 connected to a 230 volt supply is:

   a. 50A

   b. 45A

   c. 40A

   d. 32A

2   A correction factor of 0.725 is applied when the overcurrent protection is provided by a:

   a. BS 88 fuse

   b. BS 1361 fuse

   c. BS 3036 fuse

   d. BS EN 60898 m.c.b.

3   If cables are to be totally enclosed in thermal insulation for a distance greater than 0.5m a correction factor is applied of:

   a. 0.6

   b. 0.5

   c. 0.4

   d. 0.3

4   The length of run for selecting conduit size is taken to be the:

   a. total length of run

   b. distance between bends

   c. distance between draw in points

   d. distance between the origin and first bend

5   If a 75 × 25mm trunking is installed the maximum number of 4mm overall diameter cables we can install using the space factor calculation method is:

   a. 82

   b. 74

   c. 67

   d. 41

Selecting systems, equipment and enclosures

4

RECAP

Before you start work on this chapter, complete the exercise below to ensure that you remember what you learned earlier.

● Before choosing a wiring system for a particular installation the person responsible for the _____ should be fully aware of any _____ influences which may be present.

● BS 7671 contains tables which provide a _____ of the various external influences in _____.

● The _____ Code classifies the level of protection provided by enclosures against the ingress of _____ and _____.

● Classification of the level of protection provided by _____ against mechanical _____ may be determined using the _____ Code.

● In the formula $I = \frac{P}{V \times cos\pi}$ P is the _____ in _____, $cos\pi$ is the _____ factor and

I is the _____.

● When selecting protective devices the _____ of the device must be _____ to or _____ than the _____ of the _____.

● When selecting the conductor size the minimum _____ is determined by using the _____ value _____ by the applicable _____ factors.

- When determining conductor size, C_a is the _____ for _____ temperature and C_g is the _____ for _____ .

- When designing an installation _____ may be applied when calculating the _____ demand.

- The maximum permitted voltage drop for a single phase installation supplied from the public _____ is 3 per cent for _____ and 5 per cent for _____ circuits.

- The earth fault loop impedance for a system can be determined using the formula:
  $Zs =$ _____ $+ ($ _____ $)$.

- In the formula $S = \frac{\sqrt{I^2 \times t}}{k}$ I is the value of _____ current and t is the _____ taken to _____ .

- The capacities of _____ sizes of conduit and trunking may be determined using _____ of _____ .

- For non-standard arrangements of trunking, capacities are determined using the _____ factor calculation. For a trunking the maximum space to be occupied by cables is _____ per cent.

LEARNING OBJECTIVES

This chapter considers the selection of wiring systems and equipment for electrical installation. You will need to refer to manufacturers' information, BS 7671 and IET Guidance Note 1, when you are working through this chapter. You may also find the IET On-Site Guide helpful.

On completion of this chapter you should be able to:

- State the criteria for correctly selecting wiring systems, equipment and enclosures as appropriate for:

  - lighting systems

  - power circuits

  - distribution systems

  - environmental control/building management systems

  - emergency management systems

  - security systems

  - CCTV, communication and data transmission systems.

Part 1 Lighting systems

The study guide *Installing Electrical Systems* in this series identifies the types of wiring systems and some of their uses. In this chapter we will consider the selection of the wiring system for typical applications in electrical installations.

For installations in dwellings the standard wiring system is flat insulated multicore cables for the circuits within the building. This cable is also used for a number of commercial and industrial locations. It is a very versatile wiring system and with suitable additional mechanical protection where appropriate can be used in a wide variety of installations. However, this does not automatically mean flat multicore cable is a suitable alternative system and a combination of the use and environmental conditions must always be considered.

Let's begin by looking at the requirements for lighting systems. There are some common installation systems used for lighting and the selection of the system will be based upon a number of factors:

● the extent and complexity of the lighting system
● the nature of the building
● the intended use of the building
● the requirements of the client.

We should first consider the basic lighting circuit options for simple lighting installations and for this we shall use the example of an installation carried out in flat multicore and cpc cables.

Basic lighting circuits

The basic lighting circuit is generally a three-plate wiring system which may be carried out using a suitable junction box. The circuit diagram

for this is shown in Figure 4.1 and the practical circuit in Figure 4.2.

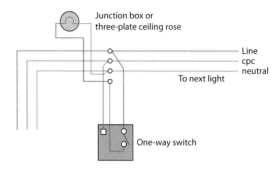

Figure 4.1 *Three-plate lighting circuit diagram*

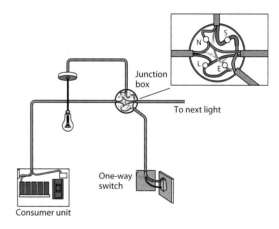

Figure 4.2 *Four terminal junction box*

Note

BS 7671 requires all such terminations in equipment to be accessible unless the equipment is identified as complying with BS 5733 and marked as 'maintenance free' with the symbol (MF) and installed in accordance with the manufacturer's instructions.

Three-plate ceiling roses are commonly used in the installations in dwellings and plug-in 3 plate versions are widely used in commercial and industrial installations.

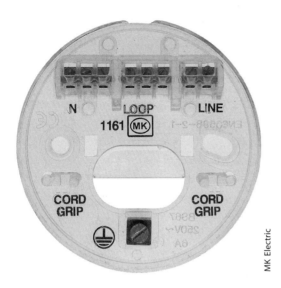

Figure 4.3 *Three-plate ceiling rose*

Figure 4.4 *Typical plug in ceiling rose*

The linking of the conductors may also be carried out at the switches providing the connections are contained within suitable terminations.

Two-way switching

On occasions it is necessary to have two switches controlling one light. This often happens on staircases or on landings and halls and in these situations two-way switches are used. The circuit is usually wired using three-core and cpc cables when carrying out this type of installation in flat multicore and cpc cables. The circuit diagram for this is shown in Figure 4.5. This is known as the

conversion method, as by the use of three-core and cpc cable and a change of switch a one-way light may be readily converted to a two-way.

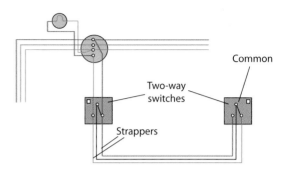

Figure 4.5 *Two-way (conversion method) lighting circuit diagram (cpc's omitted to switches for clarity)*

Intermediate switching

Where more than two switching positions are required an intermediate circuit is used, as shown in Figure 4.6. The intermediate switch has four terminals which is used for all switches between the two-way switches fitted at either end of the switch line. The internal switch connections are as shown in Figure 4.7.

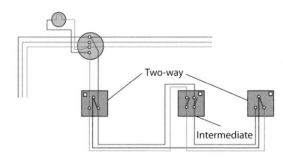

Figure 4.6 *Two-way and one intermediate switch circuit diagram (cpc's omitted to switches for clarity)*

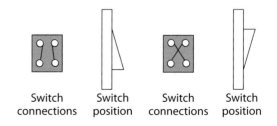

Figure 4.7 *Intermediate switching positions*

Note
Where cable cores coloured other than brown are used as switch wires they should be correctly colour coded using brown sleeving or tape to indicate that they are line conductors.

These basic circuits can be modified by the inclusion of presence sensors, photocells, passive infra red detectors and energy saving measures such as daylight reduction. The basic circuits remain the same.

Having considered the basic requirements for simple lighting circuits we need to select an appropriate installation system. The systems available to us include:

● flat multicore and cpc cable
● lighting trunking
● SWA cables
● conduit and trunking
● mineral insulated metal sheath cables (MIMS) and FP cables
● modular wiring systems.

Flat multicore and cpc cables are suitable in locations where they are not subject to adverse conditions or mechanical damage. Additional protection may be installed to enable these cables to be used in some more onerous locations.

With suitable precautions they may be used in commercial installations, such as above suspended ceilings, but adequate support needs to be provided. This could involve cable tray or other support systems and so the installation becomes more costly and subsequently not ideal. Cable csa is a standard configuration, as we found in the previous chapter, and so earth fault

loop impedance and possibly voltage drop may create an issue.

This type of cable is ideally suited to most installations in dwellings and small commercial locations.

Lighting trunking is ideally suited to locations where long runs of lighting are to be installed and the containment system for the cables can be readily installed and may be surface mounted. This is predominantly in commercial and industrial locations where such installation methods are possible and acceptable. This system provides a dedicated containment for the lighting system and support for the luminaires. It is robust and versatile and allows the use of single core cables and so offers more flexibility in conductor sizing for the designer. It is unsuitable for installations in dwellings.

copyright Legrand Electric Limited

Figure 4.8 *Typical lighting trunking*

SWA cables are often used for locations where a dedicated circuit is to be installed and the system is unlikely to need alteration or modification. High bay lighting is often carried out using this cable, with fixings direct into the structure or attached to steel girders and the like. The advantage of good mechanical protection is often the reason for selection, particularly in locations where the risk of mechanical damage is quite high. It is not appropriate for dwellings.

Conduit and trunking are often used in industrial locations and may be used in larger commercial buildings. These have the advantage of providing mechanical protection for single core cables, shared routes for other circuits such as power and socket outlets and versatility for the installation of additional circuits or rewiring existing circuits. This system is often difficult to conceal as the containment system does need to be accessible for drawing in cables. It is unsuitable for installations in dwellings.

Mineral insulated metal sheath cables (MIMS) are costly and require particular installation skills and so tend to be expensive to install. On the plus side they have excellent fire resistance properties, are robust and compact in size compared to other cable systems. They are ideally suited for locations of national, commercial, industrial or public significance, such as national museums and cathedrals. MIMS may be used for life protection systems such as emergency lighting, where the equipment is to continue to perform under fire conditions. FP cables are lower cost alternatives which have fire performance rated insulation and internal aluminium sheathing and the construction and material used allows the cable to continue to perform under fire conditions. These cables will continue to perform providing they are not disturbed under fire conditions. This requires the cable to be suitably supported throughout with fire rated cleats or saddles. This system is not often used in general installations.

Modular wiring systems are used in many commercial office buildings where they provide a flexible system with the facility to provide sophisticated control systems. As a plug and play system it provides a great deal of flexibility and adaptability for the user. This type of installation may be used in dwellings to provide a high degree of control but is expensive and is not common. Savings for commercial concerns in terms of power consumption and lowering carbon footprint can make these systems cost effective in a relatively short period. The system may require additional support such as cable tray to prevent damage to the interconnecting cables.

Distribution board
The male connector on the Master Distribution Box being connected into the female socket on the distribution board.

The MDB has been installed on the wire cable tray, the home run cable has been run back to the distribution board. Extender leads are being plugged in to provide a supply to power and lighting loads.

Figure 4.9 *Typical modular system*

Try this

A two-way lighting circuit is to be installed in a steel conduit system using single core cables. Draw a simple circuit diagram for this lighting circuit where there will only be two strappers between the two-way switches. The switch line will go to one two-way common terminal and the line to the other two-way common terminal.

Try this

List the most appropriate system to be used to install each of the following:

a   a row of fluorescent lights in a factory production area

_____

b   lights in a loft extension to a dwelling

_____

c   a lighting column in a car park where the cable is to be buried in the ground

_____

Part 2 Power systems

Power circuits include both electrical equipment and socket outlet circuits and we need to select an appropriate system for the location. The most common power circuit systems include:

- skirting trunking
- dado trunking
- bench trunking
- modular wiring systems
- powertrack and busbar trunking
- SWA cables
- conduit and trunking
- MIMS and FP cables
- flat multicore and cpc cable.

The three varieties of trunking, **skirting**, **dado** and **bench**, all provide a containment and mounting system for accessories. Whilst they may be used for multicore cables they are generally used for single core cables. As the names suggest each trunking is designed for use in particular locations. Their use is primarily associated with the installation of socket outlets but they do provide a containment system for fixed equipment wiring. In many cases these trunkings are segregated (contain more than one compartment) which allows other systems to be installed within the same trunking system.

The common application for these containment systems are in commercial and industrial installations. The skirting and dado trunking are commonly used in office locations where the system selected depends on the use of the installation. Executive style offices often include skirting trunking whilst in more general office areas the access to accessories may require dado trunking. On many occasions it is the client's aesthetic preference. The bench trunking is

generally used in workshop and laboratory locations to allow ready access to accessories.

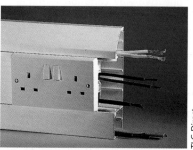

TLC Direct

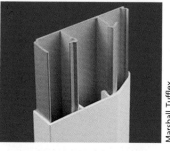

Marshall Tufflex

Marshall Tufflex

Figure 4.10 *Skirting trunking, dado trunking and bench trunking*

We have considered the advantages of **modular wiring systems** related to lighting systems in Part 1 of this chapter and the same applications and advantages will apply to the power system applications.

Powertrack and busbar systems are basically a prewired distribution trunking which uses copper bar conductors and plug in units to tap off power supplies where needed. These systems are commonly used in industrial locations to provide a versatile distribution system for plant and machinery. The tap off units incorporating protective devices allow for a number of types of equipment with different power requirements to be supplied via a single power distribution system. The powertrack system is frequently used below raised floors in commercial premises to supply socket outlets and equipment. The use of bar conductors means there is no wiring to be carried out up to the tap off points.

SWA cables are frequently used to supply individual items of equipment in industrial locations. The fact that they are robust and readily fixed to a variety of surfaces or installed in ducts or directly in the ground makes them a very versatile option. They are commonly used for individual items of equipment and particularly where these are added to an existing installation. These are used as an alternative to conduit and trunking systems in smaller industrial locations but determining the overall number of circuits and the available space for cables within the building structure is a deciding factor.

Conduit and trunking is a common installation method in commercial and industrial installations. It provides a containment system for single core cables and can be used for a number of circuits sharing a common route. The use of plastic conduit and trunking in areas where the risk of mechanical damage is not high can prove economical in terms of installation time and material with fewer specialist tools required. Steel conduit will provide a robust containment system suitable for industrial locations, and which may be used in commercial premises, warehouses and the like.

MIMS or FP cable systems are used to supply power to safety services such as sprinkler pumps, firefighters' lifts, smoke vents and alarm systems. These are selected for their performance under fire conditions and the equipment associated with safety services must continue to function in the event of a fire. They may be used to supply other items of equipment but this is not common.

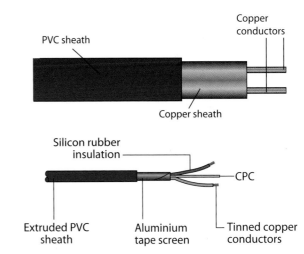

Figure 4.11 *MIMS and FP cables*

Flat multicore and cpc cables are one of the most common methods used to supply socket outlet circuits in dwellings and commercial properties. The advantages and applications are similar to those discussed for lighting systems.

Socket outlet circuits

The ring final circuit

The most common socket outlet circuit used in domestic installations is the ring final circuit. As the name implies, the circuit starts and finishes at the same point and should form a continuous ring. The line starts and finishes at the same protective device (fuse or circuit breaker), the neutral starts and finishes at the same connection on the neutral bar, and the circuit protective conductor starts and finishes at the same connection on the earth block. Each socket outlet on the ring has at least two cables to it. This means that there must be at least two conductors in each terminal. Most socket outlets now have two earth terminals to enable them to be used on circuits where there is an earth leakage current in excess of 3.5mA and clean earth systems.

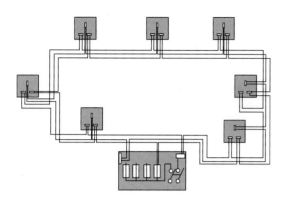

Figure 4.12 *A ring final circuit*

In general there should be a separate ring final circuit for every 100m² of floor area. We must remember that the maximum load that can be connected to a ring protected by a 32A fuse or CB is around 7.6kW, and the number of circuits selected accordingly.

Non-fused spurs

Where a socket is required at a point away from the run of the ring circuit cables a non-fused spur (Figure 4.13 to 4.15) may be used. This is a single cable run just to this outlet. The cable conductors for a non-fused spur must not be of a smaller cross-sectional area than that of the ring conductors. Usually in domestic premises a 2.5mm² conductor is used with a 1.5mm² circuit protective conductor.

The non-fused spur may be connected from:

- a socket on the ring
- a junction box connected onto the ring, or
- the consumer unit or distribution board.

A spur must not be more than one single or one twin socket outlet.

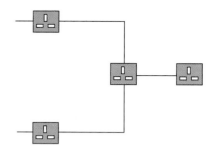

Figure 4.13 *Non-fused spur from a 13A socket outlet*

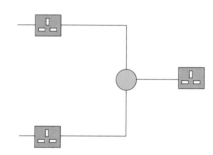

Figure 4.14 *Non-fused spur from a junction box*

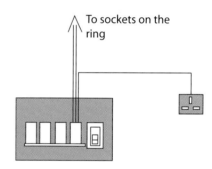

Figure 4.15 *Non-fused spur from a distribution board*

Radial circuits

Radial circuits, unlike ring circuits, do not return back to the supply point. They are basically a loop in and out circuit. As the current distribution is not as good as the ring circuit there are tighter limitations on their use.

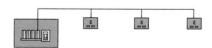

Figure 4.16 *Radial socket outlet circuit*

Try this

List the most appropriate system to be used to install each of the following:

a   a new kiln circuit to be installed in an existing workshop

_____

b   socket outlets in a general office with solid floors

_____

c   a number of lathes in a metal turning factory

_____

d   a fire sprinkler pump in a public building

_____

Part 3 Distribution systems

Distribution circuits are used to supply additional distribution boards which are often remote from the origin of the installation. These are often referred to as sub-mains. By the nature of the distribution circuit these usually only occur in complex installations where there are a number of distribution boards supplied from a single incoming supply.

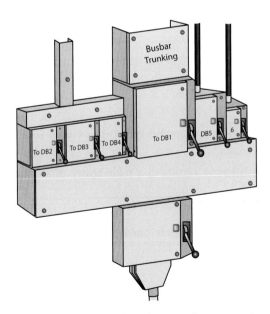

Figure 4.18 *Typical distribution layout using a variety of systems*

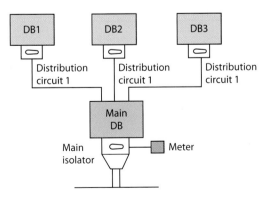

Figure 4.17 *Typical distribution circuit configuration*

Distribution circuits

The principal systems used for these distribution circuits are:

- busbar trunking
- SWA cables
- MIMS.

The decision as to which one will be used depends upon the purpose of the distribution circuit, the construction of the premises and load.

Busbar trunking is often used in multi-storey buildings where a large rising busbar is installed vertically through the building. At each floor there will be tap off boxes supplying distribution boards and then the final circuits. As we established earlier the busbar may also be used to supply a number of items of equipment from a single distribution busbar. Whilst this system is effective and efficient the busbar is not flexible and whilst it can be supplied with bends and sets it is not suited to installation in restricted access areas.

SWA cables are frequently used as distribution cables as they have the advantage of being flexible and so easier to install within the confines of buildings. They are also suitable for distribution circuits between buildings where the cables need to be installed in ducts or directly in the ground.

As we discussed earlier the **MIMS cable** may be used for distribution circuits where they supply safety services to ensure continued function in the event of fire.

Single core cables in conduit and trunking may be used for distribution circuits but the considerations of load and physical conductor size, particularly with respect to volt drop make these systems less common in all but the most compact of installations.

 Try this

List the most appropriate system to be used to install each of the following:

a   distribution circuits in a multi-storey office block

_____

b   to supply a separate building within a complex

_____

c   the distribution board supplying fire fighting equipment

_____

Part 4 Management and alarm systems

Environmental control and building management systems

Environmental control and building management systems are used to control equipment within the building environment. These include air conditioning, dust control, odour and fume control and ventilation.

Many of these systems operate using twisted pair cable in a variety of forms and the type of cable and the csa of the cores will affect the distance from the control unit to the furthest point on the installation. For example, a typical 0.2mm^2 U/UTP cable would be suitable for a maximum length of 100m.

There are a number of different types of cable and each is classified by the type of construction. Table 4.1 identifies the cable type and the screening used for both the cable and the individual pairs.

Table 4.1 *Types of twisted pair cables*

Cable type	Cable screening	Pair shielding
U/UTP	none	none
U/FTP	none	foil
F/UTP	foil	none
S/FTP	braiding	foil
SF/UTP	foil, braiding	none

The abbreviations used in the cable types are:

● TP: twisted pair
● U: unshielded
● F: foil shielding
● S: braided shielding.

Most of the cables have a plastic insulation and sheath and the type of cable to be selected depends upon the type of circuit and the level of segregation required.

We have considered the types of cables used for these types of systems and their installation methods previously. These included CY, SY and YY, braided flexible and LAN cables, all of which may be used in the environmental and building management control systems. There is more information regarding these cables in Part 6 of this chapter.

Alarm and call systems

There are some basic circuits which apply to most alarm and call systems and it is worthwhile looking at the basic circuits here.

Open circuit systems

The simplest circuit is that used on front doorbells, for it only contains one push, one sounder and source of supply and the cable to connect them together. The push completes the circuit when it is pressed and is known as a 'push to make' type. The sounder may be a bell, chimes or a buzzer, but for simplicity we will continue to use the bell symbol.

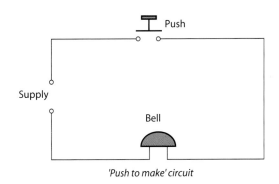

'Push to make' circuit

Figure 4.19 *'Push to make' circuit*

If an additional push is required in this circuit it must be connected in parallel with the first one.

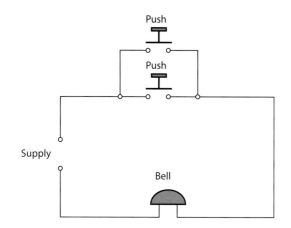

Figure 4.20 *Two call points in parallel*

Instead of 'push to make' circuits, other detection devices may be used to set off an alarm.

This type of circuit has many uses but has the problem that if a conductor is broken the whole system is out of action.

Closed circuit systems

When a sounder circuit is used for alarm systems it is more likely to be a closed circuit system. This means that the whole detection circuit is complete until something breaks it and sets off the alarm. To make the circuit practical a relay is used to divide the detection circuit from the alarm sounder circuit.

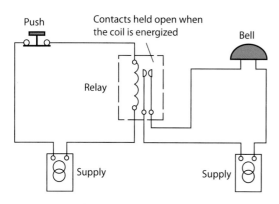

Figure 4.21 *Closed circuit system*

This relay is basically the switch that makes the circuit when the alarm is to be sounded. When the circuit is healthy the relay contacts are held apart by the magnetic field of the relay coil. This coil is energized all the time the detector circuit is complete. As soon as any part of the detector circuit is opened the alarm is sounded. Extra detectors in this circuit are connected in series with the first.

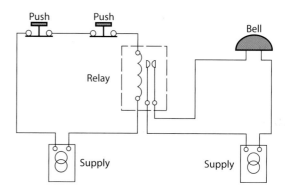

Figure 4.22 *Two detector points in series*

These normally closed circuits are often used for intruder and fire alarms. The detectors on intruder alarms may be foil strips on windows, contacts on doors, pressure pads, movement sensors or many other devices. On fire alarms they may be heat detectors, smoke detectors, flame detectors, rate of temperature rise sensors or straightforward manually operated smash glass contacts.

Figure 4.23 *Standard break glass call point unit*

Try this

Draw a circuit diagram for a:

a normally closed circuit with four call points

_____

b normally open circuit with four call points

_____

Part 5 Emergency management systems

Emergency lighting

Emergency systems also include emergency lighting. This needs to be examined from several different points of view. First, are the emergency lights to have their own emergency power supply or will this come from a central source? Next we need to determine whether the emergency lighting should be on all the time even when there is not an emergency. In this case it is referred to as 'maintained', or if it is only required to come on when the main supply fails, as 'non-maintained'.

Central supply system

This may consist of a central battery bank, which consists of secondary cells, which are constantly on charge. In a very large installation the central supply could be a standby generator. Either method would have its own distribution system and circuits wired through to where the emergency lights are required.

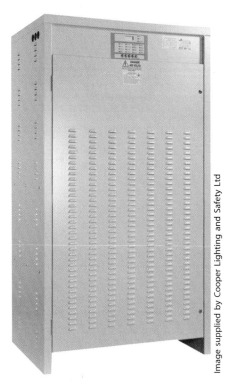

Image supplied by Cooper Lighting and Safety Ltd

Figure 4.24 *Battery unit for centrally controlled emergency services*

Local supply systems

It is often more practical to have special luminaires that have their own power source, i.e. self-contained luminaires. These can then be wired into the standard lighting supply circuit. These luminaires consist of a small battery-charging unit, batteries, relay and lamp. The batteries are constantly on charge all of the time the mains circuit is working correctly. When the mains supply fails the internal batteries take over.

Figure 4.25 *Emergency luminaires with their own batteries and charger*

Maintained lighting

In public areas, such as theatres, the emergency signs have to be illuminated all of the time. Usually in these emergency signs the lamps are supplied by the battery which, under normal conditions, is being constantly charged. When the mains supply fails the batteries continue to keep the lamps illuminated.

Non-maintained lighting

In a non-maintained circuit the lights are only used when the mains supply fails. In luminaires that have their own batteries contained within them, a relay switches the lamp on to the battery when the supply fails.

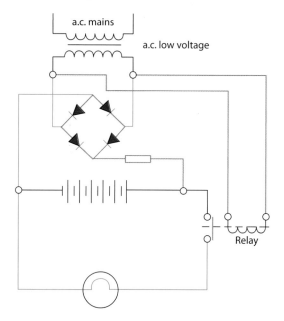

Figure 4.26 *Non-maintained system*

Fibre optics and LED lighting are often used for emergency lighting systems. Fibre optics systems comprise fibre optic cables connected to a central projector containing a light source. The light source is connected to the emergency power supply. High intensity light from the lamps is transmitted down the optical fibres in the cable to the lighting points at floor or ceiling level.

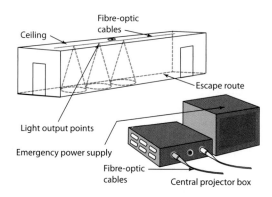

Figure 4.27 *Fibre optic emergency lighting system along a corridor*

As we discussed earlier, fibre optic cables require special care during the installation, termination and testing processes.

The advantages of this type of system are:

● There is no current flow in the fibre optic cables and so no heat is produced and there are no magnetic fields generated around them. This makes them suitable in areas where –
  – electromagnetic disturbances are to be avoided (data and single transmission etc.)

  – there is a risk of fire or in explosive atmospheres

● A single light source is required for a large area and the type of lamps used provide long life for the system and makes maintenance easier as the light is in a single accessible location

● As there is no electrical current flowing and the fibre optic cables are waterproof they may be used in exposed or hostile environments without risk.

Try this

a State two types of emergency lighting system

  1. _____

  2. _____

b State one application for each of the systems in a. above

  1. _____

c State two types of cables which may be used for these systems if they are to perform under fire conditions.

  1. _____

  2. _____

Part 6 CCTV, communication and data transmission systems

Closed circuit TV, communication and data transmission systems

The types of cables used for these systems include coaxial cables, data cables – CY, SY and YY, braided flexible, LAN cables. We have covered the construction of these and their use earlier. There is some additional information related to the cable types used for data transmission systems which is relevant to their selection for particular applications.

Table 4.2 *Common Cat type cable information*

Category	Type	Frequency bandwidth	Applications	Information
Cat 3	U/UTP	16MHz	10BASE-T and 100BASE-T4 Ethernet	Not suitable for speeds above 16 Mb/s so mainly used for telephone cables
Cat 5	U/UTP	100MHz	100BASE-TX and 1000BASE-T Ethernet	Common in most current LANs
Cat 5e	U/UTP	100MHz	100BASE-TX and 1000BASE-T Ethernet	Enhanced Cat5. Same construction as Cat5, but with better testing standards
Cat 7	S/FTP	600MHz	Telephone, CCTV and 1000BASE-TX in the same cable and 10GB BASE-T Ethernet	Four pairs, S/FTP (shielded pairs, braid-screened cable)
Cat 7a	S/FTP	1000MHz	Telephone, CATV and 1000BASE-TX in the same cable and 10GB BASE-T Ethernet	Four pairs, S/FTP (shielded pairs, braid-screened cable)

Table 4.2 contains brief details of the most common data cables and some information on their general applications.

CSC Cables

Figure 4.28 *CAN-bus cable*

Controlled Area Network (CAN) is a system used in many industries where complex controllers are required such as programmable control systems, building control systems and industrial control systems. The system does not address the equipment on the system but the messages themselves and so can deal with a large number of items of equipment. The CAN-bus system features high transfer at speeds between 1 Mbits/second at around 40m and 5Kbits/sec at 10 Kilometres.

Various forms of twin twisted pairs are used in the control industry and we shall look at some of the variations here. The variation in type relates to the level of shielding required to reduce electromagnetic interference for the particular application. The shielding can be applied to the individual pairs or collections of pairs, the whole cable may be screened (shield around all the pairs combined) and a combination of these is also used. The shielding is generally earthed in order for it to be effective and an earth wire is normally included in the cable. We will look at the various types next.

Unshielded twisted pair (UTP)

Unshielded twisted pair cables are used in many telephone and Ethernet networks. A common colour coding for the core pairs consists of one of the cores in solid colour, the other core the same colour and white so the pairs can be readily identified. On large telephone systems 25-pair cables are common whilst general domestic systems utilize smaller numbers such as the 4-pair shown in Figure 4.29.

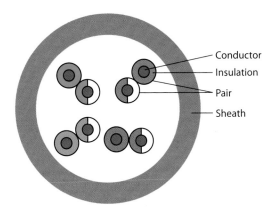

Figure 4.29 *Typical UTP cable*

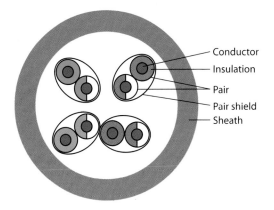

Figure 4.31 *U/FTP cable format*

Telephone company distribution cables laid in the street may contain hundreds of pairs which are divided into smaller bundles each having different twist rates which helps to reduce crosstalk.

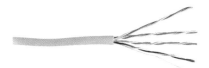

Figure 4.30 *Typical UTP cable showing different twist rates*

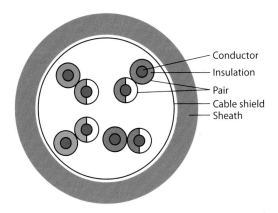

Figure 4.32 *F/UTP cable format*

UTP cable is also commonly used in computer networking data cables for short to medium runs because of its low cost compared with other options such as the fibre optic cables. It may also be used in security camera applications.

The other cable types which may be used are identified in Table 4.2 and their construction shown in Figure 4.31 to 4.33.

Many modern systems use fibre optic cables for these applications and, whilst we did consider these earlier, here is a brief reminder of their construction and advantages.

The conductor strands are made of optically pure glass as thin as a human hair (125 microns or 0.125mm diameter), arranged in bundles (with many strands), and they may be used to carry

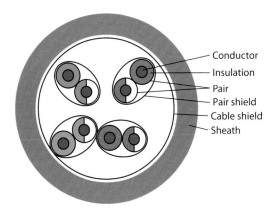

Figure 4.33 *S/FTP cable format*

digital information (in the form of light signals) over very long distances.

Fibre optic cable is constructed with a core of thin glass fibre. Where the light travels, an outer cladding of optical material surrounding the core

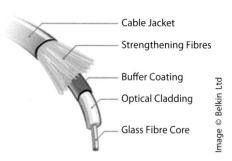

Cable Jacket
Strengthening Fibres
Buffer Coating
Optical Cladding
Glass Fibre Core

Image © Belkin Ltd

Figure 4.34 *Typical fibre optic cable construction*

reflects the light back into the core and an outer covering of plastic buffer coating protects the fibres from damage and moisture.

The main advantages of fibre optic cable are that it:

● is less expensive than copper
● has less signal loss than copper

● has a lower power rating
● is non-flammable – no electric current through fibres
● is lightweight and flexible.

The type of cable to be used will depend upon the characteristics of the building, the requirements of the system and the desired performance. The specification for this will generally be provided by the system designer.

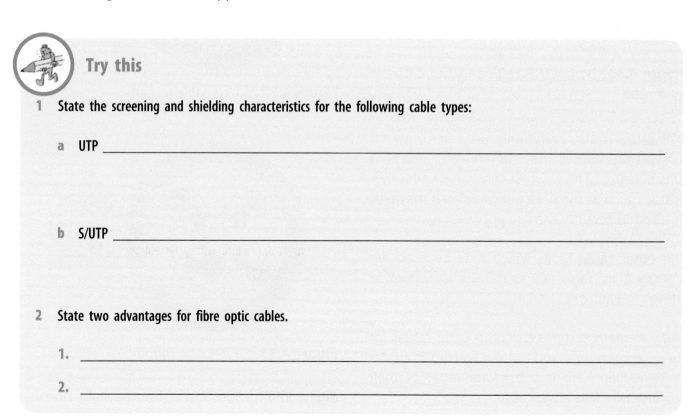

Try this

1 **State the screening and shielding characteristics for the following cable types:**

   a UTP _____

   b S/UTP _____

2 **State two advantages for fibre optic cables.**

   1. _____

   2. _____

Congratulations, you have now completed the final chapter of this study guide. Complete the self assessment questions before progressing to the End Test.

SELF ASSESSMENT

Circle the correct answers.

1   The most common arrangement for a domestic lighting circuit is:

   a.   double pole
   b.   two place
   c.   three-plate
   d.   single pole

2   Where a light is to be controlled from either end of a corridor the type of switches to be used are:

   a.   one-way
   b.   two-way
   c.   three-way
   d.   intermediate

3   An additional ring final circuit is to be installed to supply desks in an existing office building with solid floors and plasterboard ceilings. The most appropriate installation method is:

   a.   steel conduit and trunking
   b.   SWA cables
   c.   MIMS cables
   d.   dado-trunking

4   A distribution circuit has to be installed to supply each floor of a multi-storey office building. The most approriate wiring system to use is:

   a.   MIMS
   b.   SWA cables
   c.   busbar-trunking
   d.   conduit and trunking

5   One advantage of fibre optic cables over copper conductors is that they:

   a.   are more rigid
   b.   have less signal loss
   c.   have a higher power rating
   d.   are more expensive

End test

1. A three-phase, four wire system has a voltage between line conductors of 440V. The line to neutral voltage is:

☐ a. 1320V

☐ b. 762V

☐ c. 254V

☐ d. 147V

2. In order to balance the load the DNO connects the single-phase supplies to dwellings:

☐ a. on different phases

☐ b. on the same phase

☐ c. between phases

☐ d. across phases

3. In a complex installation sub-distribution boards are often located near the centre of the area being supplied. The reason for positioning in this location is to:

☐ a. maximize the length of the circuit cable

☐ b. minimize the length of the circuit cable

☐ c. standardize the location or each area

☐ d. make the installation process easier

4. A firefighter's switch is primarily installed to provide:

☐ a. isolation

☐ b. remote control

☐ c. functional switching

☐ d. emergency switching

5. The term isolation means that an installation or circuit is disconnected from:

☐ a. the main earthing terminal

☐ b. the neutral conductor

☐ c. all sources of supply

☐ d. the line conductor

6. Z_s represents the earth fault loop impedance that is:

☐ a. external to the installation

☐ b. for the circuits combined

☐ c. for the complete system

☐ d. within the installation

7. Earthing in an electrical installation connects the main earthing terminal to all:

☐ a. extraneous conductive parts

☐ b. exposed conductive parts

☐ c. metalwork in the building

☐ d. structural metalwork

8. **Main protective bonding in an electrical installation connects the main earthing terminal to:**

   - ☐ a. extraneous conductive parts only
   - ☐ b. exposed conductive parts only
   - ☐ c. metalwork of the installation only
   - ☐ d. structural metalwork only

9. **The earth fault loop impedance of a circuit is 1.21Ω and the nominal voltage (U_0) is 230V. The fault current required to cause a protective device to operate within the required time is:**

   - ☐ a. 278A
   - ☐ b. 231A
   - ☐ c. 229A
   - ☐ d. 190A

10. **The maximum disconnection time for a final circuit which is part of a TN system and is protected by a 20A protective device is:**

    - ☐ a. 5s
    - ☐ b. 2s
    - ☐ c. 0.4s
    - ☐ d. 0.2s

11. **The DNO quoted maximum external earth fault loop impedance (Z_e) for a TN-C-S system is:**

    - ☐ a. 21Ω
    - ☐ b. 5.5Ω
    - ☐ c. 0.80Ω
    - ☐ d. 0.35Ω

12. **The maximum earth fault loop impedance for a 30mA RCD to operate within the required time is:**

    - ☐ a. 100Ω
    - ☐ b. 167Ω
    - ☐ c. 500Ω
    - ☐ d. 1667Ω

13. **The current drawn by a 3.2kW load connected to a 200 volt supply is 20A. The power factor is:**

    - ☐ a. 0.55
    - ☐ b. 0.6
    - ☐ c. 0.75
    - ☐ d. 0.8

14. **The current drawn by a 230V 2.3kW load with a power factor of 0.8 is:**

    - ☐ a. 12.5A
    - ☐ b. 10A
    - ☐ c. 8A
    - ☐ d. 3A

15. **A 230V domestic electric cooker has a power rating of 13kW. The load current for the circuit, after diversity has been applied, will be:**

    - ☐ a. 56.52
    - ☐ b. 46.52
    - ☐ c. 23.96
    - ☐ d. 13.96

16. The correction factor for ambient temperature is 1 when the ambient temperature is:

- ☐ a. 0°C
- ☐ b. 20°C
- ☐ c. 30°C
- ☐ d. 40°C

17. The maximum voltage drop permitted for a 230V AC final circuit connected at the origin of the installation and supplying a heater 30m away, if the supply is from the public distribution system, is:

- ☐ a. 6.9V
- ☐ b. 11.5V
- ☐ c. 13.8V
- ☐ d. 18.4V

18. A circuit supplies a load at a distance of 50m from the origin of an installation supplied at 230V from the public distribution network. If the resistance of the line conductor is 4.61mΩ/m at 20°C the voltage drop in the circuit when a load current of 20A flows will be:

- ☐ a. 21.25V
- ☐ b. 13.8V
- ☐ c. 11.06V
- ☐ d. 9.92V

19. A single phase circuit has the following characteristics: Pfc = 350A, disconnection time = 0.1s, k = 115. The minimum cross-sectional area of the protective conductor is:

- ☐ a. 1.0mm^2
- ☐ b. 1.5mm^2
- ☐ c. 2.0mm^2
- ☐ d. 2.5mm^2

20. A 75 × 50mm trunking contains 54 × 2.5mm^2 conductors and a number of 4mm^2 cables are to be installed in the same trunking. The following factors apply. Trunking = 1555, 2.5mm^2 = 12.6 and 4mm^2 = 16.6. How many additional 4mm^2 conductors can be installed in the trunking?

- ☐ a. 93
- ☐ b. 60
- ☐ c. 52
- ☐ d. 37

21. When installing cables in a steel conduit containment system:
   (i) There must be sufficient air circulation around cables installed.
   (ii) During installation no damage must be done to conductors, insulation or enclosure.

- ☐ a. only statement (i) is correct
- ☐ b. only statement (ii) is correct
- ☐ c. both statements (i) and (ii) are correct
- ☐ d. both statements (i) and (ii) are incorrect

22. The method used to determine the capacity of non-standard size containment systems and conductors is:

- ☐ a. space factor
- ☐ b. proportional factor
- ☐ c. rating factor
- ☐ d. diversity factor

23. The ceiling rose shown in Figure 1 is a:

☐ a. plug in

☐ b. two plate

☐ c. double pole

☐ d. three plate

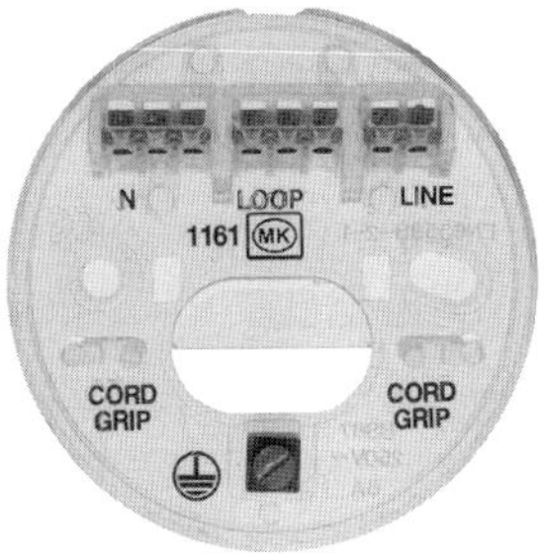

Figure 1

24. The most suitable type of installation system used for long straight rows of fluorescent luminaires in a workshop is:

☐ a. lighting trunking

☐ b. busbar trunking

☐ c. power track

☐ d. SWA cables

25. A number of high bay luminaires are to be installed in an existing loading bay. The building is constructed with an A section roof of steel beams. The most suitable wiring system to use is:

☐ a. conduit and trunking

☐ b. lighting trunking

☐ c. powertrack

☐ d. SWA cables

26. Which of the following statements is true for a type U/FTP twin twisted pair cable?

☐ a. no screening or pair shielding

☐ b. no screening and foil pair shielding

☐ c. foil screening and no pair shielding

☐ d. foil screening and foil pair shielding

27. An intruder alarm system is normally wired as:

☐ a. ring circuit

☐ b. open circuit

☐ c. closed circuit

☐ d. looped radial circuit

28. A fire sprinkler pump is to be installed in the basement of a public building. The most appropriate type of cable to supply this pump will be:

☐ a. steel wire armoured

☐ b. flat twin and CPC

☐ c. U/FTP

☐ d. MIMS

29. In a non-maintained emergency lighting system the luminaires are:

☐ a. only operational when the supply fails

☐ b. operational at all times

☐ c. only operational when the fire alarm operates

☐ d. operational only during the hours of darkness

30. One advantage of fibre optic cables over copper conductors is that they:

☐ a. are more rigid

☐ b. have a higher signal loss

☐ c. have a higher power rating

☐ d. are less expensive

Answer section

Chapter 1

Try this Page 10

- 719V
- 398V
- 191V

Try this Page 17

1 a) 400V ac for heavy plant and equipment, large motors and heating loads, etc.

   b) 230V ac for single-phase loads such as socket outlets and lighting.

   c) 50V ac extra low voltage for control equipment.

   d) 12V ac SELV for controls and equipment in special locations.

2 a) 11kV

   b) 400/230V

   c) 230V

Task Page 23

a) 113A

b) 300A

c) 400A

d) 160A

Try this Page 24

2 the circuit protective conductor – the main earthing terminal – the earthing conductor –

the supplier's neutral terminal – the PEN conductor – the star point of the supply transformer – the transformer winding – the supplier's line conductor – the circuit line conductor to the point of fault.

Crossword Page 25

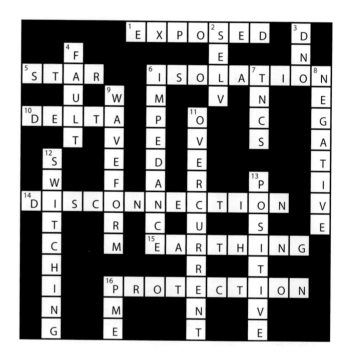

SELF ASSESSMENT Page 26

1 c) TN-C-S
2 c) 277 A
3 b) short circuit
4 c) high ac current
5 a) external to the installation

Chapter 2

RECAP Page 27

- impedance   low   fault
- terminal   PEN   TT system
- transmission   11   33   11   230
- current   zero
- 230   single-phase
- 400   divided
- 25
- live   short   overload

SELF ASSESSMENT Page 54

1 c) the water installation pipe work
2 c) 0.4 seconds
3 a) bimetal strip
4 b) sensing coil
5 d) additional earth electrodes

Progress check Page 55

1   b) 433V
2   a) 400/230V
3   d) no current at all
4   c) 31 A
5   b) balance the load on the DNO's equipment
6   d) 2m
7   d) carry for an indefinite period without deterioration
8   a) overload
9   d) low impedance
10 d) the fuses will provide earth fault protection
11 a) exposed conductive parts
12 a) main protective bonding conductors
13 b) safety electrical connection – do not remove

14 a) 0.66Ω
15 d) 0.2s
16 c) 0.80Ω
17 b) solenoid
18 c) silica sand
19 c) earth fault current
20 c) 500Ω

Chapter 3

RECAP Page 58

- electrical   touched
- protective   terminated   point   each
- bonding   extraneous   earthing
- Supplementary   shock
- Z_e 0.8   0.35
- healthy   builds   time
- short   quickly   high
- overcurrent   system   minimum
- overload   thermal   magnetic   short
- earth   into   out of   comparing
- fault   impedance   path   general mass of earth

Try this Page 65

sunlight

low temperatures

rain/snow etc.

flaura

corrosive substances (fertilizers etc. and animal faeces and urine)

mechanical damage from plant and equipment

Try this Page 69

1   25 A
2   4.35 A

Try this: Crossword Page 79

Try this Page 81

$I_b = 13.04A$

$I_n = 16A$

Minimum $I_t = 22.86A$

csa $= 2.5mm^2$

Try this Page 84

Answer $= 80.25A$

$8 \times 100W = \dfrac{800}{230} = 3.48A$

$2 \times 80W = \dfrac{160}{230} \times 1.8 = 1.25A$

$1 \times 32A = 32A$

$18kW = \dfrac{18000}{230} = 78.26A - 10A = 68.26$

$\times \dfrac{30}{100} = 20.48A + 10A = 30.48A$

$3kW = \dfrac{3000}{230} = 13.04A$

Total $= 3.48 + 1.25 + 32 + 30.48 + 13.04$

$= 80.25A$

Try this Page 88

Answer $= 4.0mm^2$

$I_b = \dfrac{7000}{230} = 30.43 \therefore I_n = 32A$ and

$I_t = \dfrac{32}{0.94} = 34.04A$

$4mm^2 = 38A$ method C and mV/A/m

$= 11mV$

Volt drop $= \dfrac{11 \times 30.43 \times 30}{1000}$

$= 10.04V \leq 11.5V$

Minimum csa $= 4.0mm^2$

Try this Page 90

Does not comply

$Z_s = Z_e + \dfrac{((R_1 + R_2) \times 30m \times 1.2))}{1000}$

$= 0.34 + \dfrac{((3.08 + 4.61) \times 30 \times 1.2)}{1000}$

$= 0.34 + \dfrac{276.84}{1000} = 0.617\Omega$

Max tabulated $Z_s = 0.57\Omega$ and as 0.617Ω is greater than maximum 0.57Ω the circuit will not comply.

Try this Page 95

$Z_s = Z_e + \dfrac{((R1 + R2) \times I \times 1.2)}{1000}$

$= 0.4 + \dfrac{(7.69 \times 25 \times 1.2)}{1000} = 0.4$

$+ \dfrac{230.7}{1000} = 0.6307\Omega$

$Pfc = \dfrac{U_0}{Z_s} = \dfrac{230}{0.6307} = 364.67A$

Disconnection time = 0.1s

K=115

$$S = \frac{\sqrt{I^2 \times t}}{k} = \frac{\sqrt{364.67^2 \times 0.1}}{115} = \frac{\sqrt{13298.42}}{115}$$

$$= \frac{115.32}{115} = 1.002 \text{mm}^2$$

Minimum csa 1.002 so a 1.5mm^2 conductor

Try this Page 98

1 $\frac{1146}{22.9} = 50$

2 $(4 \times 21.2) + (12 \times 18.1) + (30 \times 12.6) + (36 \times 9.6) = 84.8 + 217.2 + 378 + 345.6 = 1025.6$

50 × 50mm trunking has a factor of 1037 so is the smallest that can be used.

Try this Page 99

Space for cables = 60 × 60 = 3600 × 0.45 = 1620 mm^2

Space for 1 cable $= \frac{\pi \times 3.2^2}{4} = 8.04 \text{mm}^2$

Total number of cables $= \frac{1620}{8.04} = 201.49 = 201$ cables

Try this Page 104

1 15 cables
2 NO. 14 cables are the maximum

Try this: Crossword Page 105

SELF ASSESSMENT Page 106

1 a. 50A
2 c. BS 3036 fuse
3 b. 0.5
4 c. distance between draw in points
5 c. 67

Chapter 4

RECAP Page 107

● design   external
● classification   Appendix 5

- IP solid bodies liquids
- enclosures impact IK
- power watts power load current
- I_n equal greater I_b load
- I_t I_n divided rating
- factor ambient factor grouping
- diversity maximum
- network lighting power
- Z_e $R_1 + R_2$
- fault time disconnect
- standard tables factors
- space 45

Try this Page 113

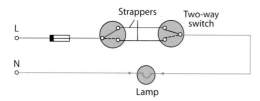

SELF ASSESSMENT Page 127

1 c) three-plate
2 b) two-way
3 d) dado trunking
4 c) busbar-trunking
5 b) have less signal loss

End test

1 c) 254V
2 a) on different phases
3 b) minimize the length of the circuit cable
4 d) emergency switching
5 c) all sources of supply
6 c) for the complete system
7 b) exposed conductive parts
8 a) extraneous conductive parts only
9 d) 190A
10 c) 0.4s
11 d) 0.35Ω
12 d) 1667Ω
13 d) 0.8
14 a) 12.5A
15 c) 23.96
16 c) 30°C
17 b) 11.5V
18 c) 11.06V
19 a) $1.0mm^2$
20 c) 52
21 c) both statements (i) and (ii) are correct
22 a) space factor
23 d) three plate
24 a) lighting trunking
25 d) SWA cables
26 b) no screening and foil pair shielding
27 c) closed circuit
28 d) MIMS
29 a) only operational when the supply fails
30 d) are less expensive

Glossary

ADS Automatic disconnection of supply

Bonding Main protective bonding connects the extraneous conductive parts to the main earthing terminal. Supplementary protective bonding connects exposed and extraneous conductive parts together in a specific location

Cable type TP Twisted pair
Cable types U Unshielded
Cable types F Foil shielding
Cable types S Braided shielding
CAN Controlled area network
CB Circuit breaker
CPC Circuit protective conductor
CSA Cross-sectional area

Discrimination Where protective devices are selected and arranged to minimize the number of circuits disconnected from the supply should a fault occur
Diversity An allowance which may be applied where the entire connected load is unlikely to be used at the same time. Knowledge of the type and use of the installation is essential when applying diversity
DNO Distribution Network Operator

Earth fault loop impedance The impedance of the total current path taken under earth fault conditions
Earth fault loop path The path through which the earth fault current flows
Earthing The connection of exposed conductive parts to the main earthing terminal and then to the source earth
ELV Extra low voltage (maximum 50V ac or 120V dc)
ESQCR Electricity Safety, Quality and Continuity Regulations

FP Fire performance
FSTP Halogen free double shielded cable

GN1 IET Guidance Note 1 Selection and Erection

HBC High breaking capacity

IK Code IEC Standard IEC 62262 for the level of protection against mechanical impact
IP Code Ingress Protection code for the level of protection against ingress of solid bodies and liquids
Isolation Cutting off of an installation, or circuit, from all sources of electrical supply to prevent danger
IT A system of electrical supply where there is either no connection of the supply to earth or the system has only a high impedance connection and an insulation monitoring device monitors the impedance. Not used in the public supply network

LED Light emitting diode

MCCB Moulded case circuit breaker
MET Main earthing terminal
MIMS Mineral insulated metal sheath cables

Overcurrent An overcurrent is when a larger than intended electric current flows through a conductor, leading to excessive generation of heat, and the risk of fire or damage to equipment

PFC Prospective fault current
PME Protective multiple earthing

RCBO Residual current circuit breaker with over-current protection
RCD Residual current device

Secondary distribution Distribution systems which operate at 11kV
SELV Separated extra low voltage
SSTP Screened fully shielded twisted pair cable
Switching A means of controlling the supply of electricity

Tertiary distribution DNO distribution systems which operate at 400/230V

TN-C The TN-C earthing arrangement is rarely used and it is one where a combined PEN conductor fulfils both the earthing and neutral functions in both the supply and the installation

TN-C-S A supply system in which the earth provision is provided by the DNO using a combined neutral and earth conductor within the supplier's network cables. The earth and neutral are then separated throughout the installation. These systems are referred to as TN-C-S or PME systems

TN-S A supply system in which the earth provision is provided by the DNO using a separate metallic conductor provided by the Distribution Network Operator (DNO). This provision may be by connection to the metal sheath of the supply cable or a separate conductor within the supply cable

TP & N Triple-pole and neutral

TT A supply system in which the DNO does not provide an earth facility. The installation's exposed and extraneous metalwork is connected to earth by a separate installation earth electrode and uses the general mass of earth as the return path

UTP Unshielded twisted pair

Z_e The earth fault loop impedance external to the electrical installation

Z_s The system earth fault loop impedance

Index: Planning and Selection of Electrical Systems Unit Five